Crafts from the Countryside

John L. Jones

David & Charles

Newton Abbot   London
North Pomfret (Vt)   Vancouver

ISBN 0 7153 7049 9
Library of Congress Catalog Card Number 75–10516

Set in 11 on 12 point Plantin
and Photoset and printed in Great Britain by
REDWOOD BURN LIMITED, Trowbridge & Esher
for David & Charles (Holdings) Limited
South Devon House Newton Abbot Devon

Published in the United States of America
by David & Charles Inc
North Pomfret Vermont 05053 USA

Published in Canada
by Douglas David & Charles Limited
132 Philip Avenue North Vancouver BC

Contents

List of Illustrations

Introduction

The quality of the craftsman's product is inseparable from the quality of the materials in which he works. He can only achieve the highest expression of his skills when his material is dependable, sound and tractable.

Though much of the craftsman's material, what one might term the craft-crop, is grown and harvested expressly for craft use, some of the best material, which has served the needs of craftsmen over the centuries flourishes without the nurture of any human hand. Norfolk reed, the elite material for the thousand-year-old craft of the thatcher, grows wild and abundant in the marshlands and river shallows of the Eastern Counties. Rushes too are another very old and important wild craft-crop found and harvested in the wet meadows and marshes of our countryside.

There is, however, much more to the craft-crop than just growing and harvesting. Many of these crops demand lengthy and specialised post-harvest preparation embodying a degree of experience and skill which makes this processing virtually a craft in its own right. The osier for example has to undergo an involved process of curing and modification which radically changes the harvested material before it reaches the hand of the creating craftsman. On the other hand the seed head of the fuller's teasel is used in the cloth-finishing factories in a virtually unprocessed form. This is a rare example of a plant product used almost unaltered as a tool. Even so the growing, harvesting and curing of teasels is almost a craft in itself.

Wild or cultivated, processed or not, all the crops and the crafts described in this book, have one thing in common. Their roots lie deep in the soils and traditions of our countryside: in the river banks of East Anglia, which as well as rushes and reeds, produce gleaming willow wood for our best cricket bats; in the hop yards and gardens of Hereford and Kent, gay for generations with the inter-mingling accents of town and country; in the orchards of Gloucestershire where perry trees, big as oaks, literally span the centuries, yielding fruit for the ancient craft of farmhouse perry-making; in the beds of lavender, peppermint, opium poppies and henbane, of Lincolnshire, Nottinghamshire, Huntingdonshire and Surrey; in the walled fields of the Cotswolds with their tall flax in breathtaking blue flower; in the downs of Wiltshire, Dorset and Sussex where English dewpond-makers conjured up water from the porous chalk. Two of the crops in this book come from the prolific seas which surround us: the hundreds of tons of porphyra harvested each year off the rocks along our stormy western seaboard; and the millions of elvers taken each spring from the crowding hosts washed into the Severn estuary.

The purpose of this book is to describe the rich partnerships of crop and craft which have developed over the years, many of which are cornerstones of our rural tradition. Happily most of these crops and their associated crafts are still to be found, often unchanged and flourishing in their place of origin.

Fagging hook in hand, rush farmer Tom Arnold harvests soft rushes on the banks of the Great Ouse

1 Soft Rushes

The burly, pipe-smoking figure, floating down the Great Ouse in the fenman's flat-bottomed boat, quietly asserts the survival of a centuries-old tradition. Tom Arnold is Britain's biggest processor of the English rush. Each year, throughout the month of June, he plies the river, continuing a family rush-harvesting tradition that goes back to the days when cargo-carrying fen-lighters, linked together in ponderous quintets, glided behind a 'fest horse' (as that time-honoured river traction unit is locally known.)

Tom's destination on these June mornings is one of the long rustling meadows of green cylindrical rushes which rise lushly from the rich riverine silt. A short-bladed sickle, the rushman's fagging hook, in hand, he draws together an armful of the tall jointless stems and severs them close to the base. The close cut is important because the bottom portion of the rush, the strongest part, is the best for weaving. Great care is also taken to keep the 5–10ft high stems as straight as possible. Cutting goes on until the barge, sinking lower and lower in the water, can take no more and is ready to be propelled back to the landing stage with a combination of muscle and motor.

Harvesting the rushes continues well into July. While they grow in most wet places and on the verges of most slow-flowing rivers, some of the finest specimens of the wild rush (*Juncus effusus*), are harvested each year from these banks of the Great Ouse. The rush farmer rotates his wild rush plantations as though farming a crop, cutting them in alternate years and then resting each cut section for another season. In this way the rush stands are kept luxuriant, growing tall and thick and straight. His bane is a wet summer. Like the haymaker he is best served by a hot, dry June; for a late harvest means that the rushes, like herbage stems, mature past their best and become 'woody' and brittle.

Like hay as well, the rushes must be cured and dried. If they remain damp for long, the stems become blotchy and discoloured. In a normal season the rushes, leant against wooden racks on the river bank to catch the sun and wind, are left to dry for about three weeks. After drying, they are stored indoors and kept away from the strong sunlight which accelerates fading. When it comes to selling, the rush merchant's unit of measurement is the 'bolt', a narrow sheaf of the dried material bonded in two places with rush ties.

Rushwork articles in some form are found in most houses today. The continued use of these table mats, shopping and work baskets, waste paper baskets, plant holders, wine bottle covers, light footwear soles, seat holders,

7

seat bottoms, even rush furniture indicates the survival of a centuries old but still flourishing domestic craft.

About two dozen rushes are needed for a handsome and durable table mat 9 in in diameter. As is the case with most craft material harvested in wet places and subsequently dried, the stems have to be well moistened before they are used for weaving. The only really essential tool for rush weaving is the rush threading needle, the rest can be improvised.

Rushes are an essential item in the craft of the cooper, or barrel maker, for though the metal barrel lined with fibre glass has largely ousted its wooden cousin in a variety of usages, the cooper's cask is still used, in the making, maturing and movement of wines. Tom Arnold's father always reserved his best rushes for his coopering customers and put them aside under the label of 'cooper's flags'.

The cooper makes use of the rush for its hygroscopic (ie moisture absorbing) qualities. It is impossible to maintain watertight joints using only curving wooden staves, for a barrel, once left empty, shrinks. By inserting rushes between the joints, the cooper ensures that when the barrel is filled, the absorbent pith of the rush swells up and seals the joints. The process of inserting rushes into a joint with a flagging iron to repair a leaking barrel is often called 'chiming the flag'. The chime of the barrel is specifically that

Rolling out the cooper's barrel at the village fete. Rushes keep the barrel joints watertight

portion of staves extending from the croze – the groove near either end of the staves where the head is fitted – to the rim of the cask.

Common though rushwork articles are in the house today, the use of rushes was, in bygone days, a matter not merely of taste but of necessity. A widespread feature of marshes and moors the country over, rushes lit cottages all over the land. The rind was stripped from the cylindrical stalks, with two narrow longitudinal strips left intact to keep the pith together. The peeled rush was then repeatedly dipped into melted fat or tallow, possibly with a little melted wax added, until the grease round the absorbent pith was thick as a pencil.

This simple rushlight was supported in one of scores of different designs of holders, some prestigeously ornate, some plainly utilitarian. Whatever their appearance, they were all arranged on the principle that the rushlight performs best at a burning angle of about twenty degrees, giving out a steady clear illumination almost as good as a candle. The two supporting ribs of rind also prevented the light from burning too rapidly. Forty inches or so of *Juncus effusus* treated in this way, would burn for about two hours.

Gilbert White, an indefatigable observer not only of the countryside's flora and fauna but also of its customs and people, was a great enthusiast of rushlighting for the rural poor. In his letter XXVI he writes:

> In a pound of rushes avoirdupois which I caused to be weighed and numbered we found 1600 individuals. Now suppose each burns one with another only half an hour, then a poor man will purchase 800 hours of light, a time exceeding thirty three days for three shillings. Thus a poor family will enjoy five and a half hours of comfortable light for a farthing. An experienced old housekeeper assured me that $1\frac{1}{2}$ pound of rushes completely supplied his family the year round.

Rushes were also widely used to cover the hard earth floors of houses and buildings, being, in some cases, woven to form 'fitted carpets'. The cottager made do with rushes alone, but the gentry often added a little straw as well as 'nose herbs', especially the pungent sorts like mint, sage and, occasionally, lavender, to sweeten the rank smell of these crude carpets. The Renaissance sage, Erasmus, was not above complaining to a court physician of rushes, on which rained drink slops, grease, bits of food and other 'organic matter', as a major source of infection and plague. Indeed, in this regard, our forebears lived like livestock today, on a form of deep litter, but without the composting of the material, which, as it heats up, kills off the noxious bacteria.

As well as carpeting mansion, cottage, and dairy, rushes also eased the austere lot of worshippers in church. 'Rush-bearing', the carrying of rushes into churches, was a ritual in which the parish villages brought offerings. This was, especially in the North of England, a gala occasion. Wordsworth, a determined supporter of such traditional rural rituals, helped keep it alive in his parish of Ambleside and his friend, the curate, composed the 'Rush Hymn', a drearily clerical work, for these occasions. A local historian describing the ceremony on 21 July 1821 wrote:

> In the procession I observed the opium eater, Mr Barber, an opulent gentleman residing in the neighbourhood, Mr and Mrs Wordsworth, and Miss Wordsworth . . . Mr Wordsworth is the chief supporter of these rustic ceremonies.

A measure of his success is the fact that the floor of nearby Grasmere church remained unpaved until 1841. In the South West, the rush-bearing tradition is still continued in St. Mary's Redcliffe, Bristol, where, once a year the floor of the church is strewn with rushes from the Somerset marshes, for a special Whitsunday Service attended by civic dignitaries.

Soft rushes were formerly used for a multiplicity of other purposes, particularly in the Eastern counties. They were the core of cushions, church hassocks (the word hassock is derived from the Anglo Saxon word for sedge), and, with the black rush, formed part of a cheap, light horse collar which sold, a century ago, at less than a shilling apiece.

This is, of course, not the only crop which the lakes and slow-moving rivers of the eastern counties boast. Large quantities of sedge were sold in dried, fire-lighter form in the hinterland towns and the bead plant, locally known as bede-sedge (*Nertera depressa*) was used to make rosaries. But the other main wild harvest from this area is, as all the world knows, Norfolk reed (*Phragmites communis*). The finest thatching material of all (see Chapter 2), this famous plant had, however, another traditional function quite apart from its past and present use in thatching. Norfolk reed was a key material in the building of the 'fowler's pipes' that were once a feature of inland lagoons. These structures, especially common in Norfolk, were masterful examples of imaginative reed craft and of the exploitation of bird psychology, for they were designed to decoy and capture large numbers of the waterfowl which winter on the Broads.

The pipe was shaped rather like a starfish, with a natural reed-fringed pool at its centre, which might vary from five to fifty acres in area. From this catchment area radiated a number of man-made channels or rays, like the spokes of a wheel. The rays, 6ft or more wide at the pool end narrowed to a point over a distance of up to 80yds. At intervals, across each ray and sunk in the shallow water on each side, were placed hooped iron arches which diminished in height from over 6ft at the pool end to a mere 2ft above the ground at the end of the pipe. Over and between these arches was slung a strong, heavy net of cord which was sunk into the reedy ooze on each side. Each ray was in effect a long, slanting, tapering cage with a roof and sides of net and a base of shallow water.

Some of the most effective pipes had as many as a dozen rays. Waterfowl invariably prefer to take flight into the wind whenever possible so that the existence of a number of rays meant that at any one time, the chance of one or more of these tunnels having the wind blowing down towards the centre pool was greatly increased. The pipes set to exploit the North-easter were invariably the most profitable, and invariably brought the birds in large numbers.

A principal factor in the effectiveness of the pipe was the craftsman's exploitation of reed. A long curving barrier, beginning at the central pool and continuing right down the ray, was built to form a duck-proof screen on both sides of the net which became smaller as the height of the ray itself reduced. At regular intervals on one side, the two-foot reed walls were extended at right angles for several feet, while the end of the ray was left unscreened. To man or bird looking up the cage, the outer containing walls of these little right-angled reed bays were invisible because they were obscured by the curve of the higher screen. It had all the appearance of a series of natural, open breaks in an open-ended stretch of reed.

With the pipe built and ready, the next stage was to set the trap. For two months before the wildfowling season began, domestic ducks with wild duck plumage were trained to come to the sound of a low whistle. Apart from the decoy ducks, the ruse required a small, light-coloured dog, the 'piper'. It was trained to run along the foot of a barrier darting in and out of the little 'bays' in the reed. The decoys soon became accustomed to the little dog's antics as he trained near their feeding ground. All was ready by the time of the autumn equinox when the decoy ducks were taken to the central pool and enticed into the rays a few times to accustom them to their new surroundings.

Around noon on a day when there were enough wild birds on the pool, the fowler, his dog, and his assistant, moved into the chosen ray. Carrying smouldering turves to obliterate their smell, they took up position. The wild fowler hid with his piper near the first pocket in the wall of reeds, the assistant closer to the mouth of the rays. The familiar low whistle then brought the trained ducks into the mouth of the ray and scattered food enticed them further inside.

Waterfowl will invariably swim after decoys and, as the mass of teal, widgeon and mallard came paddling in, the hidden wildfowler at the other end began to put his piper through his disappearing act. Duck, and especially the teal with which the Broads abound, are compulsively drawn to the antics of a dog and, as the little piper pursued his in-and-out routine, the curious wildfowl were drawn further and further into the trap.

Meanwhile the decoys, uninterested in this familiar spectacle and having eaten the bait barley, returned to feed in the central pool. The wild birds continued swimming down the ray until they were well under the net, when the assistant, entering the pipe behind them through the reed screen, startled them into headlong flight down the tunnel. When they reached the 'open' end, they were stopped short by the 'purse net' which the wildfowler had placed across the end of the ray.

These operations were often spectacularly successful. In the winter of 1859, one pipe on the Broads netted almost 2,000 duck — a tidy catch at a time when a pair might fetch eight shillings on the London market. These rewards were deserved, however, for piping duck demanded both imagination and a craftsman's attention to detail. Subtle construction of the reed tunnels was vital. They had to look natural enough to override the suspicions of birds made wary by centuries of harassment and hunting. As well as possessing patience and skill to train his dumb accomplices, the wildfowler needed to be an expert in the exploitation of wildfowl psychology. All in all, he needed to combine the silence, stealth, timing and determination of the huntsman with the care and the skill of the craftsman.

2 Craftsman's Straw

In Somerset and Wiltshire, the straw is 'long straw', in Devon the straw is 'reed', and in Norfolk the reed is simply the finest thatching material in the western world. Materials and the terms describing them vary from area to area, and, as we shall see, these arcane and apparently contradictory distinctions are indeed important to the local thatchers who understand them. To the uninitiated bystander, gazing at the colour, symmetry of form and perfection of finish that bespeaks a good thatched roof, it probably doesn't much matter which material is used or what the local craftsmen call it.

Blissful though such ignorance may be, the thatcher and his history are quite as interesting to study as his work is beautiful to look upon. In Britain today, he is busier almost than he has been since the eighteenth century. Because of this revival, the best thatching material is both expensive and scarce, and the experience and skill of our five or six hundred trained craftsmen is at a premium. In the past, the young aspirant to the thatcher's trade acquired his skills by following a family craft tradition. Today, such is the interest and demand for the expertise of the thatcher that there is already one training school – with a small but well-filled intake – run by the Council for Small Industries in Rural Areas (COSIRA). This does not alter the fact, of course, that most young thatchers still graduate into the master-thatcher class by working from an early age with established practitioners of the craft.

The three main categories of thatch, fleetingly and confusingly mentioned above, are long straw, Devon reed and Norfolk reed. The least processed of them, long straw, is wheat straw more or less in its natural state. Not all wheat straw will do, however, and the choice of the right wheat variety is the first vital aspect of growing thatching straw. The wheat has to be a medium or long-strawed variety. It must be winter-sown to provide the lengthy growing season necessary for it to reach the right length and strength. The crop must not be seeded too thickly or fed with excessive nitrogen. The crowding which follows heavy seeding, and the excessive vegetative growth which accompanies high nitrogen dressing, both shade the base of the growing plants so bleaching and weakening the lower sections of the stem. The soil must also be reasonably fertile; the best thatching straw can never be grown on poor land, because the wheat plants must have good root anchorage to safeguard against falling over or 'lodging' on the ground.

The field producing long straw (or straw for Devon reed), must be cut by the reaper and binder. Because the ears will have time to ripen and harden in the stook, the wheat is ideally cut when the stems are still slightly tinged with green. The sheaves are put into the stooks and, after a period in the field – there is an old adage that they require three clear Sundays in stook – are usually taken direct to the threshing machine. There the opened sheaves are carefully fed, one by one, into the drum which separates the grain from the straw. The earless straw which emerges is then usually passed through a tying machine which bonds the straw together into bundles. The straw is now ready for the long-straw thatcher.

For thatchers of the pre-war generation there were certain favourite wheats whose names became household words: the delightfully titled 'Little Joss', the Jacobin-sounding 'Elite du Peuple', and the uncompromisingly English 'Squarehead's Master'. Compared to today's these were relatively low yielding varieties. Happily for the thatcher, one of the modern wheats, which produces the best long straw and Devon reed, 'Maris Huntsman', is also one of the highest yielding.

Wheat reed is a rather more specialised product than long straw and requires different preparation. After hauling from the field, the sheaves are passed through a machine known as a 'reed comber', which fits on top of the conventional thresher. A series of revolving drums with hooked tines removes the grain and leaf from the wheat, without the straw having to pass through the beaters of the threshing drum. The straw emerges intact and lying in one direction. The combed straw is then either conveyed to a mechanical tying machine or flows into the reed cradle where it is collected for hand tying into 28lb bundles or 'nitches', the standard unit and description of combed wheat straw in Devon. After tying, the butts of the nitches are thumped once or twice on the spot board to ensure they are tight and tidy and, after trimming, are ready for sale to the reed craftsman. The old method was to comb out the straw by hand, using one of a variety of methods of holding or suspending the stems, before pulling them against an iron comb. This was usually a wet-day job done in the barn, and the old Dorset reed-combing method features in a memorable scene in Hardy's *Tess of the d'Urbervilles*.

Both traditionally and in today's practice, the different methods of preparing long straw and Devon and Norfolk reed are matched by differences in thatching technique. Long-straw thatching, which is most widely practiced in the corn-growing counties like Wiltshire, has as its most distinctive feature the application of the straw to the roof in 'yealms'. These tight bundles of straw are 14–18in wide and 4–6in thick. The yealms are prepared on site by the thatcher from his opened-up bundles (or sometimes his loose heap of tipped straw), after the material has been thoroughly wetted to make it pliant and easy to handle. However, before he begins to lay his

This long straw thatch on a Wiltshire cottage still looks good after twenty years

standard yealms, the long-straw thatcher prepares some special double-thickness yealms. These bundles, bonded round with a twist of straw, are known as 'bottles'.

The thatcher begins his task by laying his first bottle of straw diagonally across the right angle formed by the eaves and the gable. As successive bottles of straw are added and butted tightly together, they are either tied to the roof battens with tarred cord or, most likely, held in place by the 'sway' – a hazel rod, several feet long, which is placed across the surface of the bottles. The swayed bottles are then fastened to the roof structure by the use of iron hooks which are driven over the sway, into the rafters below. At the same time, the craftsman keeps his individual straw bottles married closely together by driving in hazel 'spars'. These split-hazel or willow rods with sharpened ends are bent into the shape of long-armed staples.

Before he begins to lay main courses along the roof proper, the long-straw thatcher threads a thin layer of loose straw over the battens of the roof – rather like an underfelt – in order to produce a suitably tidy appearance when the roof is seen from the inside. The yealms of straw are now laid in successive courses, rammed firmly upwards into each other, hooked to the rafters, and sparred and combed together, to form a thick interlocking conglomerate of tightly packed straw. During this process the thatcher makes constant use of his 'needles' to hold the yealms temporarily in place or to carry the tarred cord into the thatch. He also makes use of the side rake, in a combing, beating action to dress down the finished sections and rake out all loose straws.

At each and every stage the vigilant eye and shaping, combing hands of the thatcher are coaxing, shifting, adjusting to ensure the correct angles and perfect overlapping of the courses. He is especially careful in the valleys – the place of meeting of the various roof slopes – in the moulding of the yealms round dormers and along the ridging, where the straw must make a watertight join with the stone or brickwork. Each time he descends his ladder to load up his yoke with yealms, the thatcher will stand back and check that there is no blemish in lay and line.

Round the chimney and along the ridge, the long-straw thatcher creates a distinctive, ornamental pattern of rods which is one of the hallmarks of his method. He uses a combination of 'liggers' – horizontal hazel rods 4–5ft long – spars and sways to form an ornate 'stitch' worthy of a seamstress. Finally with courses all finished, liggers laid and dressing with the side comb accomplished to satisfaction, the overhanging bottles of straw, which lie along eaves and gables, are trimmed off with his long-handled eaves knife. Sheep shears attend to any final titivation.

This is virtually the only trimming and clipping which is done on long-straw thatch. As a result, the long-straw roof retains a characteristically flowing appearance in which the straw gives the impression of having grown out of the roof. The best long-straw thatches have a brushed, wind-ruffled texture. They are as naturally efficient as they are naturally finished. Waterproof as duck's wing, unbending as an oak plank, these roofs will last up to thirty years.

All thatching of course, be it of long-straw, Devon or Norfolk reed, is concerned with providing a durable, waterproof roof covering which is cool in summer, warm in winter and easy on the eye. In short, they must achieve the same synthesis of beauty and function which is every craftsman's art. But while long-straw thatching has a natural, almost homespun appearance the other two styles, associated with wheat-reed and water-reed, have a smoother texture and 'dressier', more military appearance.

From the thatcher's point of view the principal difference between long-straw and wheat-reed thatching is that, with the latter, the straw is applied to the roof with the ends, or butts, of the stalks exposed. The attachments of hazel liggers, sways, spars and tarred cords are also virtually all concealed under the reed. The wheat-reed craftsman, like his long-straw colleague, begins by thoroughly soaking his material with water and making what he calls his 'wadds' for the eaves and gables – the equivalents of the long-straw thatcher's bottles. To attach them, a long hazel sway is nailed along the battens just inside the barge board (the piece of board that conceals the roof timbers projecting over the gable), and a length of tarred cord is used to lace the reed wadds tightly to the sway. Unlike the long-straw thatcher, the reed craftsman makes constant use of the 'leggett', a flat, short-handled, tined or grooved rectangular beater of wood, to ram the butts of the wadds upwards into each other and to keep them tight together and in perfect line and trim. From the beginning, the reed thatcher aims at a geometrical precision of fit with sharply trimmed curves and lines. The effect is almost one of starched-front severity and certainly has no element of that indefinable dishevelment which is a feature of the long-straw thatch.

This precision effect, as of a perfectly cut uniform, is perhaps even more spectacularly embodied in the work of the Norfolk reed thatcher. This wild water-reed is the most perfect of all material for this style of thatching, being fine and strong and uniform in diameter, rather like a bespoke thatching cross between long strawed wheat and tall fibre flax.

Norfolk reed grows in huge stands in the county's marshlands reaching to a height of 8ft or more. The expanses of reed are easily distinguished from the rush acres by their broad, spear-shaped leaves and the myriad brown plumes which form the seed heads. Unlike the rush which is harvested in midsummer, reed harvesting does not begin until the frosts have stripped the leaves from the stems and the reed has begun to assume its

Detail of a thatched roof in Devon, showing the brushed, 'quilly' appearance of reed thatching

superb golden winter colours. It can be a cold, sodden routine, although the cutting has been mechanised in a few places. Cutting has to go on from Christmas to spring, until the new growths or 'colts' begin to make their appearance. Hand harvesting is done with a scythe or sickle and the bundles are trimmed on a wooden spot-board.

In one sense, hard weather is the reed cutter's friend, for heavy falls of snow flatten the trash among the reed to water level, while in some difficult beds the presence of ice can provide a firmer working base. Working with his own design of scythe or sickle, the reed cutter severs the reed near the base, taking out the trash from the freshly cut material with a crescent-shaped rake and then tying it into bundles about 12in in diameter at the base. As in the case of rushes, reed beds must be regularly cut, at least every two years, in order to keep the beds disciplined, and to promote and maintain tall, orderly, acceptably weed-free growth.

By tradition, Norfolk reed is calculated and sold, not by the bundles, but by the 'fathom', which is the number of tightly stacked bundles contained inside a piece of cord 6ft in circumference. Some craftsmen include in their reed bundles, as a matter of choice, a small amount of bullrush (*Typha latifolia*), and of wild iris (*Iris pseudacorus*). An integral part of the reed thatcher's material is the giant sedge (*Cladium mariscus*), which is harvested while it is still green and before the leaves have acquired the serrated sharpness which can cut the hands like a blade. It is used for thatching the ridge of the roof and, like reed, giant sedge assumes a pleasing golden-brown colour at maturity.

Norfolk reed thatching differs much less from thatching in Devon reed than these methods do from the long straw style. In particular both have the 'quilly' perfection which comes from the technique of laying the material with the butts of the stalks exposed. But unlike the wheat-reed style, the eaves and gables in Norfolk reed thatching are not cut to shape, and this to the expert eye is one of the principal differences in finish and style. The other principal distinction lies in the use of the marshland giant sedge to form the roof ridging. Like wheat reed, the sedge has to be soaked before use and it is applied to the ridge in yealms bound tightly together by the thatcher's needles before being deeply sparred into the reed.

The sedge is kept in position by an intricate pattern of split hazel rods – 'cross liggers' – and spars which, apart from their strictly functional role, also provide in their diamond, dogtooth or herring-bone patterns a delightful design against the darker surface of the sedged ridge. While working, the Norfolk style thatcher makes continuous use of his leggett and various cutting blades – eaves hook, topping knife, bond-cutting knife, shearing hook – to produce the sharp trim and perfect edge which characterises the Norfolk style of thatch. The results of this precision toil will often last for over fifty years.

Thatching of whatever style has remained a craft of hand and eye. Rarely does the master thatcher make use of rules, straight edges or other gauges; virtually all his jobs are different and involve a continuing series of value judgements. As with all true craftsmen, his product grows to fruition as a result of a curious blend of empathy, experience and instinct. Like other crafts, thatching has its rules and the basics have to be learned, but the best thatch is never a stereotype, and invariably bears a hallmark of the individual thatcher's creative style, particularly in the detail of the ornamental finish.

When the thatching of ricks was widely practised on our farms, the straw ornament crowning the rick was also very much the hallmark of the individual thatcher. Rick thatching held an element of ritual as the final completion of harvest home, and, invariably, there was competition as to which farm could produce the smartest rickyard. The craftsman might take a week to waterproof a huge rick or cock of corn, which might have to remain dry for six months before threshing. The rick was trimmed and shaved meticulously clean with a scythe before the thatcher began his task.

Today the advent of the combine harvester and the baler has banished the corn and hay rick from large parts of Britain. The principal exceptions are the hill districts of Wales where oats sheaves are still stored in ricks or cocks for feeding whole to the outlying cattle through the winter, and also in eastern Scotland where most of our porridge oats are grown. Here the art of stack building – usually on wooden frames or on stone 'mushroom staddles' – and thatching with straw, string and spars still flourishes. The signature of the thatcher, in the form of ridge-dominating cocks, peacocks, bells, sceptres, keys, crosses or corn dollies, still signals pride in a job well done.

Like the major craft of roof thatching among the professionals, the even older craft of corn-dolly making has experienced a considerable revival among amateurs in the years since World War II. Thatching as we know it today probably dates from about the time of the Norman Conquest, though roof thatching with wild vegetation no doubt existed long before the birth of agriculture and the growing of straw crops. Corn dollies, however, have their origins in our primitive ancestor's fear of death and disaster. The earliest corn dollies were probably made in the form of female figures, and intended as propitiatory gifts to the goddess of fertility. Among some early peoples the propitiation ritual took the grimmer form of a human sacrifice, usually of a stranger seized in the vicinity of the corn field.

The weaving of straw into human figures was a feature of the harvest in

All corn used to be ricked and thatched, and a farm worker with the thatcher's skill was an important man on a big corn-growing farm.

many British counties well into the nineteenth century and, in some remote areas, even later. The dolly was usually fashioned from the last stalks of corn where the corn spirit was traditionally thought to be hiding. It was variously known as the 'kern baby' or 'neck' of corn and was carried home in triumph at the end of harvest for safe keeping until the spring sowing. As the precisely symbolic content of the ceremony disappeared, the corn dolly began to assume different shapes, satisfying the artistic itch of rural crafts-men in idle moments.

Apart from decorating ricks and making corn dollies, straw was, in the eighteenth and nineteenth centuries, also one of the most popular materials for decorating attire; so much so that, in 1872, a commentator on the cur-rent fashion scene wrote, with visible exasperation, 'Straw, straw, straw, everything is ornamented with straw from the Cap to the Shoe Buckle.'

Wherever else it may have been found, straw was, of course, most closely associated with hats. The English straw hat industry grew and boomed into a major activity, not merely in its traditional home, Bedfordshire, but also in the Eastern Counties, the South Midlands, as far south as Kent and

Devonshire and as far North as the Orkneys. The plaiting of straw brought prosperity to large sections of rural England. Indeed, there were complaints in some areas that the reward from the domestic plaiting of straw 'makes the poor saucy and no servants can be procured where this manufacture establishes itself'.

Straw plaiting rapidly became a 'rationalised' industry. The farmers grew the wheat straw (the best plaiting straw being grown on chalk downs). It was cut, harvested while still slightly green, and inspected by travelling straw dealers who bought it in the rick. The ears once removed, the stems were cut to a length of nine to ten inches, bleached or dyed, and then passed through a simple, mechanical straw sorter which consisted of a series of sieves through which the straws were jolted and graded according to thickness. The straw dealer then sold his bundles of processed straw stems either direct to the cottage workers – women and children were the chief practitioners of the craft – or from his stall at one of the many plait-straw street markets held weekly in Luton, Hitchin, Dunstable, Hemel Hempstead, Tring, Shefford, Toddington and elsewhere.

A big breakthrough in the cottage craft of plaiting was the invention of the hand-operated straw splitter. This short-handled tool with a multibladed head fixed at right angles to the handle increased production and produced finer splits than the old knife-splitting method. These straw plaits embodied a wide variety of designs and patterns, sometimes of exquisite complexity in which seven or more straws were simultaneously plaited. The plaits then were trimmed, and passed through the cottager's plait mill. The finished plaits were sold in bundles, by the score, or in coils of up to twenty yards in length, to the middlemen dealers who supplied the straw factories, or the hat-makers working at home.

England's main competitor in the straw hat trade was always Italy, for Tuscany grew a superfine wheat straw which English growers could not match, and the hats from Leghorn were always far superior to the English product which catered for the coarser end of the trade. The domestic industry in England lasted well into this century but as the task became increasingly mechanised, the cottage craft finally came to an end.

3 Fibre Flax

At certain periods in Britain's history, the call has gone out for a revival of flax growing as a matter of national urgency. In the present century the fortunes of flax have been bound up with war. The government scheme in World War 1 laid down thousands of acres. With the end of the war, flax once more sank into the doldrums. Yet this relegation has nothing directly to do with agriculture. Both soil and climate over much of Britain are eminently suitable, and, apart from hemp, make flax Britain's only commercially exploitable fibre crop.

Neither can we attribute these fluctuations to an enduring, if sporadically manifested, distrust of the crop. Flax is, in Britain, a venerable growth and one with which the country's fortunes are inextricably interwoven. Linen brought from Egypt by Phoenician traders, may first have been presented to woad-painted Britons as early as 1,000BC. The Romans contributed to the establishment of the crop with a linen-making factory at Winchester. Ireland, with its cool, moist climate and cloudy skies, was already growing flax on a relatively large scale by 100AD, and its linen was famous among the rulers of Europe three hundred years later. Linen is a recurrent subject in the chronicles of the Anglo Saxons. It is also recorded as a titheable, and so a fairly widely grown, crop in 1175 and, by the sixteenth century, was a compulsory feature of English tillage. At this time, flax was the very stuff by which our navy sailed, being an essential ingredient of sailcloth.

From the fifteenth to the eighteenth century, however, the flax-based linen industry, suffered from the monopoly of cheaper wool. This was the golden age of the fleece; linen being favoured by the wealthy, while wool was for those unable to afford the finer fabric. Then came the devastating challenge of cheap cotton.

In more recent times when the priorities of war were not over-riding, the principal deterrent to the production of home-grown flax has been the costliness of this labour-intensive crop. Until World War II, the main flax-producing countries were those with lower living standards and large reserves of peasant labour. During that war, British flax was again called upon to satisfy demands for the materials of war – medical lint, canvas, cordage, fire hose, aeroplane fabric.

Expansion was easier this time because harvesting had at last been mechanised. Flax grown for fibre differs from all other crops in that the plants have to be *pulled* up by the roots, and traditionally this had been done by hand. It was an infinitely laborious chore in which a moderately efficient worker could still pull no more than a single acre in a *week*. This scale of possibilities was overturned with the advent of mechanical flax-pullers from Belgium which, given reasonable conditions, could pull up to twelve acres a day.

Faced with the problem of suddenly producing large acreages of a crop which they had not sown for twenty years, British farmers were also able to reap the dividends of two decades of research into flax varieties which had been undertaken in Northern Ireland, still the traditional home of the world's finest linen. Seed from new varieties was available to produce flax crops yielding fifty per cent more fibre than the crops of the twenties. This war-time demand began a boom in home-grown flax which was to last for fifteen years.

The boom was built, of course, on the 'bottom' put into the enterprise by a guaranteed market – the flax processing companies were government controlled – which ensured the growers a fixed price for every ton of fibre produced. Additionally the government provided the very expensive pulling machines for harvest and also gangs of hand labour for tying the pulled crop into sheaves. Flax became a great favourite with the arable farmer, be-

Tresses of 'scutched flax' – flax fibres which have been extracted from the stems of the plant

cause it could be in the soil for less than a hundred days and still yield 3 tons to the acre and a big financial return.

Flax seed – plump, shiny, brown, oily – is sown in April, at a density of 90–112lb per acre, by a combined seed and fertiliser drill. The seedbed has to be fine enough and firm enough to ensure the more or less simultaneous germination which produces a crop of uniform maturity at pulling time. An uneven, lumpy tilth can also cut overall yields by a third. A fine bed is vital also because the grower has to aim for maximum ground coverage with about one plant to each square inch. Such close crowding encourages long fibre stems, with minimum branching.

Flax grown for fibre and linseed grown for oil seed are two different culti-vated strains of the same species, the one bred selectively for maximum fibre content, the other for maximum yields of seed. The fibre flax plant grows to a height of 3–4ft, with few side shoots being developed.

Flax makes only very modest demands of the soil and does well under conditions of only medium fertility, although it cannot withstand drought. The best fibre comes from medium length stems grown in a moist summer. The timing of the harvest is critical too, for the highest quality fibre is har-vested when the bolls are still slightly green with the base of the stem begin-ning to change colour. Pulled nearer to maturity the flax plant gives a higher yield of fibre but of a coarser quality. A typical yield in Northern Ire-land, where the growing of flax has reached a high pitch of efficiency, would be 2 tons per acre of air-dried crop, including the seed bolls.

Unlike fibre flax, the plant grown for linseed is not pulled but cut with cereal harvesting machinery – no easy job because of its tough stem – and the optimum time for cutting is when the first seed pods have become brit-tle. If a combine harvester is used, the seed bolls have to be cracked by a special attachment in order to release their seed. Both the fibre and seed crops are to some extent dual yielding in that the seed of fibre flax has a commercial value, as has the fibre of linseed.

Both crops have one thing in common, they offer an incomparable spec-tacle to the passerby. A breeze-stirred stand of flax in delicate flower has all the softness of cloud and blueness of sky. Even after the spectacular profu-sion of flower is over, the ripening crop, with its tens of thousands of tall wire-fine stems, retains something of its gossamer appearance.

Flax is, however, a subtle spectacle. It has no life at a distance and does not compare with red-chaffed wheat at sunset, firing a whole landscape with a heart-glow of burning charcoal, or a stand of rape in Maytime flower, a mirror of sunlight that literally dazzles the eye. But, to the close observer, the sight of flax in a field is a worthy intimation of the splendour of damask.

A Lincolnshire field of flax in shimmering blue flower

The harvest itself is impressive, as the machines leave an endless, curving wake of long stems, all inexorably facing in one direction. This trail of supine stems may be gathered into sheaves or 'beets' by hand, though an increasing number of self-tying machines are coming into use. Before the beeters tie the flax, it is gathered into bundles by the feet in what looks like a stylised harvest dance. After tying, the flax beets are put into stooks and left out to dry and mature. Once dry, the modern fibre flax crop is passed through a specially adapted threshing machine to remove the seed. Before the crop was 'rippled' like this, the seed had to be removed from the bolls by a sort of flailing action, not with the conventional flail, but with a cudgel-shaped wooden tool, known as a 'stamping bill'.

Flax is a 'bast' fibre, which means that the long fibre bundles in the stem of the plant are bonded by gummy substances to a woody portion which has to be removed before the fibre can be processed. These gums are dissolved by exploiting the natural process of decomposition. A number of methods are common, collectively known as 'retting'. In most English flax-growing areas, the rippled stems were laid in grass meadows for the rain and dew to dissolve the bonding gums and loosen the outer covering. 'Dew retting' might take from four to six weeks before the cracking stems indicated that the process was complete. This method tends to produce unequal results, but the old fashioned dew-retted fibre still produces some of the best and strongest linen.

In the second method, practised especially in Northern Ireland, the beets

25

were steeped in 'lint holes'. These hard-base ponds filled with soft peaty water were allowed to warm up for a few days in order to accelerate bacterial action. The beets, placed upright in the lint holes, were weighted down and left retting for up to three weeks. At the height of the season, the miasma rising from the lint holes filled the air with a foul stench of fermentation. Traditionally, the retted flax beets were opened up and placed on grass or new mown hay to begin drying out, after which, to complete the drying, they were put up into small hollow cocks built round wooden frames. They were then tied again into beets and stacked for the next stage of processing. The rich liquor from the lint holes was used on the fields as fertiliser. Today, the same basic process is carried out inside closed, warm water tanks to which chemicals may be added to accelerate the anaerobic fermentation which breaks down the lignin and gums.

After retting and drying, the flax stems have to be further processed to remove all vestige of woody substance. On English flax-growing farms and in English villages where flax dressing had formerly the status of a cottage industry, this 'scutching' process meant heating the flax stems in the 'haling house', before the crisp-dry stems were pulled through ridged wooden rollers to loosen the woody covering and expose the fibre. The scutched stems were trimmed with the flax 'swingler'. This wooden tool, shaped like a large curving knife, was about two feet long, with one thin edge and a curved bill. The fibre bundles were then combed or 'hackled', and the flax fibre was ready for sale either to the flax factory or the village flax shops.

Today the scutching is done by passing the retted and dried flax through a series of scutching turbines or fluted rollers, while passing the fibres through progressively finer sets of pins completes the hackling process. It is at this stage that the image of 'flaxen tresses' suddenly comes to life, for hackled flax fibre forms a cohering straw-tinted mass with a striking resemblance to blonde human hair.

The flax fibre, pulled, rippled, scutched, hackled is now ready to be drawn out and spun into the same kind of yarn as that used to weave the shrouds of the mummified Pharoahs. However, that ancient linen was of a fineness and quality which has never been repeated, more than 350 fibres going to form one single thread.

Flax may be the oldest fibre known to man, but this has not exempted it from harsh competition with the man-made fibres which now contend in areas where linen once reigned supreme. However, the rigid strength, heat resistance and absorbency of linen thread still make it uniquely suitable for certain manufacturing and industrial processes, and few would deny that freshly laundered linen and linen damask still provide an unrivalled combination of comfort and elegance.

4 Laverbread

As the tide recedes it may be seen, covering the rocks like a sheath of sea satin. For laver or *Porphyra umbilicalis*, one of the Red Algae, is to be found between high and low watermarks, especially on the more exposed sections of the British coastline. It shares its upper littoral habitat with other inter-tidal algae, particularly the luxurious masses of channelled sea-wrack which grow all around it in the tidal pools. In colour it varies from olive green or purplish red to light or dark chocolate or even near black depending on the age of the plant, the season of the year and the degree of exposure to sunlight between tides. Adhering to the rocks by tiny discs, its gelatinous cells allow the laver to resist successfully the scour of the strongest seas. The texture of laver can vary from relatively fleshy to translucent and membranous.

Apart from samphire, another fleshy, succulent growth in the inter-tidal zones which is sought and eaten like a sort of marine asparagus, laverbread is the only plant of the shore eaten in quantity in Britain. Moreover, the annual consumption, now about 250–300 tons, continues to increase each year. The laver for the laverbread – a free translation of the Welsh 'bara lawr' explains this misnomer – is mostly harvested along the west coast of Britain. The amount eaten by English consumers increases each year, but the bulk of the harvested laver still ends up on breakfast plates in industrial South Wales. There in the valleys it is greatly esteemed as a unique nutritional and medicinal delicacy.

Although it may be eaten in Wales, over half of the laverbread eaten each year is gathered from the west coast of Scotland, and the next biggest provider is Cumberland. Cornish gatherers also pick the weed from parts of their coastline. The laver actually harvested in Wales comes from south of Milford Haven while some supplies are received from Southern Ireland, where it is known as sloke. The importance of quick delivery of the harvest to the processors was early recognised by British Railways with the granting of special concessions. Porphyra consignments are brought south on passenger trains, at freight rates.

Laverbread is prepared for market in a score or so of small 'cottage factories' in South Wales. Processing is usually a part-time occupation to buttress the returns of smallholdings, market gardens and other, mostly rural, employment. When the partly dried laver is emptied from the sacks, the first priority is to get rid of every grain of sand. After vigorous and repeated washing, it is piled into cast-iron boiling pans.

The uncooked weed is then heavily salted and boiled for up to twelve

27

hours in a minimum of water. Less water and less boiling are needed for spring harvested laver, because the fronds are tenderer than those of the winter-gathered weed. The weed is finally ready when it has been reduced to a dark gelatinous pulp which is allowed to drain overnight. It is then put through a mincer which turns it into a homogeneous mass to which dark colouring matter is added. The end product looks rather like spinach, although even more unpleasant associations may be raised.

The flavour of laverbread – very much an acquired taste – is, not surprisingly, with something pleasantly seashorish about it, salty. It is normally eaten for breakfast, after dusting with oatmeal, and is sometimes moulded into little cakes coated thickly with oatmeal. These cakes, which perhaps explain its misleading Welsh name, are fried in bacon fat. Swansea market has a stall, famous in South Wales, which deals only in laverbread. However, the product is now also available much further afield, and is sold from cold counters in many English towns.

Laver is harvested all the year but the freelance gatherer is subject to a tantalising contrast of seasonal supply and demand. The market is firmest during winter when cooked breakfasts are commoner, but supplies are less

Varying from olive green to purplish red or dark chocolate, the texture of laver can be relatively fleshy or translucent and membranous

dependable then because the laver colonies may be decimated by gales and violent seas. Its growth and recovery rate are slower at that time of year and, of course, conditions often make harvesting difficult, sometimes impossible for the gatherer.

Some laverbread eaters also observe the oyster taboo on consumption during the 'R-less' months, a custom which probably reflects the fact that laver does lose some of its flavour from May to August. This is not only because the weed is of inferior quality. At this time, it rots more quickly in transit and the summer product can have a tendency to taint. Nevertheless there is a summer market, and laverbread is eaten by some enthusiasts all the year round.

Porphyra gatherers are invariably loners like the old wildfowlers of East Anglia and the men who today harvest the Norfolk reed in the depths of winter. The porphyra freelance is a true freebooter of the tide, seeking the edible seaweed whenever sea and tides permit, walking urgently in all weathers along miles of rock-strewn shore, plucking the beautiful weed from the rough-surfaced boulders.

In the process, the harvester develops an intimate and close relationship

Harvesting laver or porphyra on a Pembrokeshire shore

with his or her stretch of shore, knowing and nurturing the areas of abundance and quality much as a farmer does a rich home meadow or the rush gatherer his outstanding stands of wild rushes. Knowledge of the porphyra grounds and the local quirks of wind and tide, can be particularly important in winter. A gatherer, now retired, always welcomed a strong south-west wind, especially when it clashed with a receding tide, so creating a turbulence which swept the sand from the laver-covered rocks.

The weather is, of course, important throughout the year. Growth normally begins to quicken in February and by mid-April the weed is throwing out luxuriant fronds. A good week's picking then with, say, five hours between tides might net the harvester in excess of 3–4cwt. The seasonal flush, however, can be checked by a cold, wet March. If there are long periods of biting winds, the laver becomes discoloured and can fetch less from the buyers, despite the fact that any discoloration is easily rectified at the processing end by the addition of artificial dark colouring. As the summer advances, the porphyra gatherer usually concentrates on the weed nearest the low water mark, because it is exposed for a shorter period to direct sunlight and, as a consequence, has a richer, darker colour and bigger fronds.

Porphyra is a versatile growth. It never colonises on pebbly beaches or small boulders with smooth unbroken surfaces, but, given sand and suitable large, rough-surfaced boulders on which its tiny spores can lodge and anchor, germination may begin within a few hours of the spores finding a host. A few days more without storm and the porphyra is secure against all but the strongest wave action or tidal scour. Nor is it only rocks which are colonised. One gatherer describes how the hull of a wrecked ship, covered and uncovered for years by the tides, provided a fine crop of laver until it was finally broken up. Old motor tyres which are trapped in the rocks will grow porphyra, and even floating mines. Concrete emplacements and breakwaters may also be quickly colonised.

Porphyra is said to grow particularly well on rocks near an inflow of fresh water, stimulated possibly by decreased salinity and organic material from the fresh water. However, all harvesters agree that the finest growth comes from rocks freshly split by the sea and covered with sand. As the rock is uncovered by the spring tides and the rotted weed is washed away, the new growth begins with great vigour.

Algologists of an earlier age sometimes lamented the lack of interest shown by the English in the culinary and medicinal qualities of porphyra. A Victorian parson observed that 'John Bull, though so truly a man of the sea, does not take kindly to an alginic diet'. Another authority, also writing in the mid-nineteenth century, stated in the *Phycologia Britannica* that:

it might become a valuable article of diet, in the absence of other vegetables, to the crews of our whaling vessels sailing in high latitudes, where every marine rock at half tide abundantly produces it. In its preserved state it may be kept for an indefinite period in closed tin vessels.

Porphyra has a high protein content and is rich in vitamins B and C. The interest now being shown in laverbread in some West Country towns is not a new phenomenon, for it was popular in Bath as long ago as the eighteenth century, where it was sold mainly in pickled form. Eaters of laverbread in South Wales claim the dish as a valuable source of iron and an ideal laxative. It was also widely recommended, because of its iodine content, as a safeguard against goitre – a reputation that still persists. These and a host of other curative and restorative properties for which this seaweed has long been known, show us what a beneficial growth it is, and, incidentally, that ours is not the first age of the health crank.

5 Bittering Hops

The cultivated hop (*Humulus lupulus*), is grown for the resins, volatile oil and tannin found in the ripe cones or strobiles. This 'lupulin', as it is collectively known, contains over two hundred constituent compounds which are extracted by boiling hops in a mixture of malt and water – the 'wort' – in order to transfer the unique mellow bitterness and the delicate hop aroma to the beer. Hops are precious and expensive, for, although their resins and oils are only vestigially present in the finished product, they can account for almost a quarter of the total cost of materials used in the brewing process.

Some of the most spectacular hops in the world are grown in England. The secret is simple; the hop yards and gardens of the West Midlands, the Home Counties and Kent are among the very few in the world where the male hop is allowed to mix freely with the females.

In each acre of hops, some ten to fifteen males are planted among the fifteen hundred to two thousand female plants. As a result, the towering congregations of female plants, which actually produce the crop of aromatic cones, are fertilised by wind-blown male pollen. These mature into the bigger, pendulous 'frilly grapes' which characterise the English harvest.

It is quite a different story elsewhere. On the Continent, where, by reputation, they should know better, the unfertilised hops which they harvest, are smaller because, there, the male hop, whose pollen plumps the English females with seed, is a wanted criminal. Blazoned in police stations and on market hoardings, the outlawed male enjoys a notoriety as great as the Colorado beetle does elsewhere. Such enmity exists because the seed of fertilised hop females causes grave problems (as well as imparting the wrong aroma), during the brewing of the distinctive lagers which European beer drinkers favour. This contrast of attitudes outlines not only a curiosity of taste, but also a curiosity of the hop plant. It is, of course, dioecious, bearing the male and female – the staminate and pistillate – flowers on separate plants, and so may be grown seeded or unseeded.

Kent, the traditional home of English hops, still accounts for about half of the sixteen thousand acres on which hops are grown in Britain. Herefordshire and Worcestershire are the next biggest producers while Surrey, Hampshire, Berkshire and Sussex make minor contributions. A major historical reason for the choice of hop-growing areas, was the proximity of in-

(Opposite) English hops are substantially bigger than the continental variety because the cones are fertilised by male pollen

dustrial cities from which came the casual labour required to pick the ripened cones. For generations the hop yards of Hereford and Worcestershire were serviced by workers from South Wales and the Black Country; and the gardens of Kent and the Home Counties by garrulous Cockneys. This urban dimension has given hops a special place in our harvest story, for the picking of a single, large hop garden provided work for six hundred families which with all attendant friends and relations could add up to a temporary township of four thousand souls.

The annual invasions carried into Kent on the 'hopping specials' spanned well over a hundred years, and the methods of harvesting the hops changed little from the eighteenth century when, according to the *Modern Husbandman*, 'farmer William Ellis of Kent who grows 100 acres of hops runs up a little hut or shed at every one or two bins and furnishes it with wheat straw for the pickers to lie on, and a cask of small beer. And to make them proceed with the greater courage he gives each person every morning a quartern of gin.'

London hop pickers worked mostly in family units. The twining stems or bines were stripped into canvas covered wooden frames – 'cribs' in the West Midlands, 'bins' in Kent – and the picking score for each family was recorded on tally sticks, two separate cheatproof lengths of cleft wood both of which were notched identically by the picking foreman as each bushel was picked. The foreman kept one part of the cleft tally and the pickers the other half, the check stick. The picked hops were bulked into big sacks or 'pokes' in the gardens, and taken by horse and wagon to the oasts.

By the 'fifties, however, the increasing affluence of industrial workers was making hop-picking holidays less attractive and dependence on hand-picking increasingly hazardous for the growers. The take-over of the machines began to accelerate, until only one pocket of hand-picking remained, in Kent. This last outpost of a long tradition was wound up in 1968 when the river Medway rose in spate at the height of the season and spilled into the temporary township with the result that the whole population of hop pickers had to be evacuated overnight. The machines had finally taken over and the last cross-fertilising, work-and-play mingling of town and country at harvest time was ended.

Yet the advent of mechanisation has not robbed the English hop gardens of any appeal. The winter skeletons of poles and wires, the small stools, or 'hills', barely visible in the rows, still grow with astonishing rapidity into towering labyrinths, rich with the resin odours of the ripening cones, overlaid with a faint whiff of sulphur, redolent of country inns and barrels of beer. Walking among the aromatic aisles one has a sense, as with no other English crop, of an almost tropical luxuriance and energy of growth, an im-

34

pression borne out by the fact that on a hot June day, the hop bine can lengthen by more than 9in inside twenty-four hours. In one respect, indeed, the advent of the machines has actually increased the herbaceous majesty of the hop garden, for it has freed the climbing plants to be lifted on to higher wirework, out of the reach of human hands.

Until modern wirework was introduced, hops were grown round individual poles arranged in threesomes on each 'hill'. Today the seemingly identical patterns of poles and wirework vary considerably according to region. In Kent, the typical practice is to sink poles in every row spacing them two or three plants apart at a density of three to four hundred poles per acre, with 'wires' and strings interlaced to lend the Kent hop garden its characteristic appearance of a herbaceous sloping forest. In the West Midlands, there are more plants per acre but fewer poles. A well cared-for hop garden will last for fifty years.

The supporting wires themselves last a long time – up to twenty years or more – but the wire-clipped strings, round which the bines are clockwise-trained each May, are replaced annually. The strings on which the bines colonise are put on in April. In the Weald of Kent, there is an annual competition to find the most efficient and fastest 'stringers'. They formerly operated on giant stilts, the best of them finishing an acre a day, but now are more likely to work from a 'crow's nest' on a tractor.

The mechanical changes in English hop growing today are happening alongside another major change which brings to an end a grower's saga begun in 1861, a famous date in the story of English hop growing. It was in that year that a grower of Brenchley in Kent with the improbable name of Mr. Fuggles noticed a chance seedling growing in his hop garden. This seedling greatly took his eye for vigour, and the quality and size of its cones. It stood out, too, as a particularly beautiful plant, with the reddish purples of the leaf stalk contrasting vividly with the green colour of the bine itself.

Hops are easily propagated both by seed and vegetative methods and, by 1875, the provident Mr. Fuggles was in a position to effect a large scale launch of a new seedling. His judgement was endorsed and the virtues of the 'Fuggles' as a dependable variety for both grower and brewer alike caused it to spread like wildfire until, soon, it had taken over the greater part of the English acreage.

It became as much a household name among English hop growers as Victoria was among plum growers. The brewers loved the utterly dependable 'Fuggles' – and still do – with its perfect balance of bittering resins, volatile oils and tannins. The flavour and aroma imparted by the 'Fuggles' became an accepted part of the 'palate' of some of our most famous beers. Certainly the brewers would have been happy to go on with the 'Fuggles' forever.

It was the growers who had to seek a change. In 1923, the fungus disease dreaded above all others by hop growers, verticilium wilt, was diagnosed in a Kentish hop garden, and the infection began to move out from Kent like pond ripples from a stone. By the early 'sixties it had affected more than half the hop farms in Kent and Sussex, and soon reached the Hereford and Worcestershire hop yards as well.

Now the position is that the 'Fuggles' cannot be grown commercially on many farms because of the disease, and growers have, willy-nilly, been forced to substitute wilt-resistant varieties bred at the research establishments. The talk among hop growers is now of 'Tutsham' and 'Bramling Cross', 'Janus', 'Progress' and 'Alliance', 'Bullion' and, especially, 'Northern Brewer'. These new, at first reluctantly adopted, substitutes for the 'Fuggles' do, however, have attendant advantages. In particular, the female flower clusters or 'burrs' mature into firmer, denser cones, less liable to break when picked mechanically (broken cones invariably lose some of their expensive vital resins).

With the aid of a long-handled pole-knife, this worker cuts down the remaining pieces of bine to ensure that all the precious cones are harvested

These tough, modern growths also fit well into the time and motion of mechanical hop picking with its loaded trailers shuttling remorselessly from the fields with the severed bines, to fill the maw of the picking machines. To feed the machines, the bines are hung on a continously moving overhead track which passes slowly into the heart of the machine. Inside, the cones are picked with surprising gentleness by banks of spring-loaded loops mounted on rotating drums. The laterals are removed by rubber-covered rollers, loose seed and petioles blown away by powerful fan cleaners, until finally the green legions shuffle slowly out for final inspection by hand and eye, prior to being loaded into the open weave sacks – the 'pokes' of Kent are 'greensacks' in the West Midlands – for careful transporting to the drying oast.

The image of English hops is perhaps above all associated with the traditional oasts, and especially with their white witch-hat cowls, which dot the Kent countryside. Before the advent of modern power fans, these big, conical funnels played a vital role in the hop harvest, their purpose being to create an upsurge of hot air passing from the braziers through the floor of hops. They were also needed especially during windy weather to prevent any back surge of cold air into the oast.

Oast funnels are constructed to pivot on vertical spindles, which are supported on big rafters laid horizontally across the chimneys. Maintenance of a constant drying temperature is critical and most of the drying houses were built without inner staircases so as not to interfere with the rise of hot air from the braziers below. Access to the hops was usually via a stone staircase outside.

Now that few modern oasts rely on natural draught any more, but use power fans, the cowls are now only spectacular relics of the vanished age of hand-picked hops. Yet the interiors of old and new oasts alike still offer the same rich, hot spicy world at drying time. The hops are heaped on horse-hair cloths spread over the slatted floors which are built above the electric drying kilns. In the kilns, the eye-smarting, nose-tingling sulphur conditioner is burned and passed through the cones to ensure the yellow-green colour which the buyers look for, and also to preserve the precious exciting aroma. By this process the hops are reduced by hot air from approximately 80 per cent moisture to the required 10 per cent, and then left to reabsorb a little moisture from the atmosphere.

Despite all the electronic aids and alarm bells of modern units, the judgement of the oast foreman is still the vital factor in ensuring the best quality hops. Curing remains a traditional craft of eye, nose and hand, and modern gadgets have done nothing to make the oastman's inherent skill superfluous. However, the analysis of the brewers' chemists assessing the 'alpha acid' content of hops is, admittedly, an increasingly important aspect of hop quality assessment.

After curing and cooling, the hops are mechanically pressed into strong, 8ft high jute sacks. These 'pockets', as they are deprecatingly called, will hold about 168lb of hops, and are stencilled with the name of the grower, the parish, district, year, weight, variety and grower's serial number. In the old days before mechanisation, the 'bagster' stood inside the pocket and used his feet to push down the hops being shovelled in around him.

Once the hops are safely packed away into the rectangular pockets, the harvest is over. Yet, after harvest, there is little pause in the hop grower's year for, as soon as one picking is over, the winter work inexorably begins for the next. Bine remnants have to be cut off and burned. The soil has to be fed with 'shoddy', the bulky waste product of Yorkshire wool factories, which decomposes and releases nitrogen at the optimum rate. Repairs have to be made to the wirework. Earth must be moved from round the 'hills'. Replacement sets have to be ordered. Bine bases have to be pruned and earthed up.

After the winter maintenance, spring sees application of herbicides, ploughing, cultivating, fertilising, until, once again, April arrives and with it the stringing competitions of the Weald. Then comes hand pulling of infected shoots, the chemical dusting of the 'hills', removal of the first bines, the 'pipers', to encourage increased fruiting in the new growths, the all important Maytime clockwise training of the youthful bines round their appropriate strings – the most skilled of the year's operations, and usually performed by women – the removal of base leaves to discourage disease, the restoration of orderly growth after storms (many hop gardens are protected by poplar screens, evergreen hedges, or by 'lewing', a sort of netting), cultivating, fertilising, chemical dressing.

As this breathless succession of tasks is completed at the end of June, the bines are already writhing along the top wires, and the laterals reaching out for each other and joining in prickly embrace across the aisles. With the approach of autumn, the hop grower spends more and more time examining his increasingly redolent forest of cones for disease and aphids. In July and August, the picking machines are prepared and, with slight varietal differences, the roar of harvest begins again in early September when the cones are bright, yellowish green with a crisp, tissue-papery texture. Whatever other crops may be grown on the farm, hops get priority, for they must be picked when the maximum amount of lupulin is in the cones. However, the tensions of hop harvesting notwithstanding, the farm with a quota of profitable hops is always a much sought-after property, and registered hop acreage is usually sold as a separate asset.

Hops were not always so prized. In the sixteenth century, when the English began to forsake ale – the unfermented liquor of malt – and continental, hop-flavoured 'beere' or 'biere' made headway, hops were still being castigated as a 'wicked and pernicious weed' in many parts of the country. Indeed, at this time, financial penalties were enforced against both growers and users, but, by the seventeenth century, ale was out, and beer was in.

Hops are the only hardy, climbing, herbaceous perennials cultivated in Britain, and the crop was probably first introduced here by the Romans. Pliny, incidentally, gave the hop the invidious title of the 'Wolf of the Willow' because of its strangling habits of growth. However, the first truly commercial plantings appeared to have followed the arrival of the Flemish refugees who valued hops in beer, not merely as agents of flavour and aroma, but also for their preservative qualities.

British beer can be divided into three main categories, which depend principally on the type of malt used. Top-quality malting barley produces the light golden malt used in the brewing of light ale, a somewhat darker malt is used for heavier-gravity bitters, while mild beer makes use of a well-cooked, chocolate-coloured malt. It is during the boiling of the 'wort' – the mashed malt and water – that the hops are added, now mostly in the form of hop essence, or as pellets. Use of the whole, dried, fluffy cones is a thing of the past. In the opinion of some drinkers, who were happy no doubt to find the occasional bit of hop petiole or seed floating in their pints, the flavour and aroma have suffered as a result.

However, in one respect at least, the story of English hops has come full circle since the sixteenth century when we began to import French hops to flavour the new style beer. For we are once again importing the seedless continental varieties to provide flavour and aroma for British-brewed lagers, which are apparently becoming more popular in our pubs. Indeed, there have even been dark, though unconfirmed, rumours that the English male, recognisable by the two slits through which the anthers 'dehisce', or explode the fertilising male pollen may soon be fighting a rearguard battle to maintain his conjugal rights in the hop gardens and yards of England.

English brewers would have few complaints if the hop male were ousted, for the dividends of growing seeded hops – increased resistance to certain diseases, higher weights per acre, more uniform ripening of the cones – are reaped mainly by the growers. Furthermore, the seed, which can add 20 per cent to the weight of the cone harvest, and for which they have to pay the grower, is just so much expensive dross. But English hop growers are a well-organised group, bolstered by a proud tradition and, more concretely, by the Hop Marketing Board. So far, their preference for growing seeded hops has carried the day.

6 Perry Pears

A leisurely progression in late April and early May through the parishes of Gloucestershire, especially those that run up to the borders of Herefordshire and Worcestershire, provides a spectacle unique in the British countryside. Solitary, in pairs and groups, in gardens and orchards, in combes and on slopes, dominating all other fruit trees, with trunks and branches as high and wide as forest oaks, the great trees froth and foam with pink and white blossom. To further delight the senses, many of these flowering giants give out a delicate perfume in spring as well. The perry pear trees of the West Midlands are, indeed, one of the enduring glories of old England.

Perry, which is made from the pure juice of the perry pear, is one of the oldest fermented drinks in Britain and the tree one of Britain's most venerable growths. The perry pear is unique in its resistance to the trials with which other fruit varieties are beset in old age. Those in Gloucestershire span the generations like parish records, and there is no denying the old saying that, 'he who planteth perry pears truly planteth for his heirs'.

The first main planting of perry pears along the Gloucestershire/Hereford border and in the Severn Vale probably followed the arrival of the Normans. They planted seedlings, brought from France, in the laying out of William the Conqueror's estates. Paradoxically, where this giant flourished and yielded mightily, more modest growths languished, for much of the heavy alluvial land which became the traditional preserve of the perry pear is not suitable for apple trees.

The initial plantings soon spread beyond the Norman estates and, over the years, thousands of perry-pear seedlings rooted in the heavy lias clay of the Severn Vale and on some of the lighter soil bordering the Forest of Dean. Mostly, the seedlings were planted in grass to provide a bonus crop of fruit in addition to hay and grazing for livestock. This dual-purpose system worked well in an area where rainfall is plentiful and sunshine relatively abundant for both grass and fruit.

It was, however, much later that perry making came into its own. Like cider, it was given a major boost by the Napoleonic wars when wine was scarce and its consumption unpatriotic. During this period, some Gloucestershire farmhouse perries became famous and were distributed to many parts of England.

As perry making grew and flourished on the Gloucestershire and Herefordshire farms, it also supported new craft industries, especially those that dealt with stone. The farmhouse makers found that prolonged milling of the pears greatly increased the quality of the perry – their judgement has been confirmed by modern chemists, for tannin content is largely controlled by the length of the milling process. The old stone mills evolved for the purpose were, of course, made locally. These mills consisted of a huge 'runner' stone, standing on its edge, which ran inside a circular, axled stone trough known locally as the 'chace'. The millstone, which was operated by a horse harnessed to a frame, revolved hour after hour to ensure high quality perry. The raw material for the thriving local craft industry came from the Forest of Dean. Millstones for both perry and cider mills, as well as the big stone vats which held the pears, were hewn from its sandstone and millstone grit deposits.

Yet though they use the same mills, farmhouse perry making is quite a different skill from that of the cider maker. In the first place, vintage perry can be produced from single varieties. With a few notable exceptions, cider is made from a mixture of varieties because few cider apples have the balance of tannin, sugars and acids required to ferment a good unblended cider. Indeed, some single variety perries positively will not live together at all. Single pear vintages, which, unblended, are as crystal clear as spring

The 'runner stone' of the perry mill ran on its edge inside the trough or 'chace' where the pears were heaped

water, will often cloud and sour when blended with another pressing. This is not to say that perries are never blended – some have to be – but the farmhouse variety was, as often as not, made from the fruit of a single tree. The quality of perry is also more critically dependent on the balance and general quality of soil.

Perry pears differ from cider apples too in that many varieties deteriorate and rot rapidly after harvesting. The optimum stage for milling and pressing varies from variety to variety and one of the reasons for the quality of some farmhouse perry was, undoubtedly, that the farmer could get to know his individual trees as well as he knew his cows. With this knowledge, he could mill and press his pears when the fruit was 'vintage ripe', a much more limited period than that of cider apples which can hang about for weeks. In this respect, farmhouse perry making, based on individually known trees and varieties, was perhaps the nearest English equivalent to the winemaking skills of France.

After the nicely judged harvest, immediate milling and pressing the juice from the milled pulp also ensured that the perry pears, which are sensitive in this respect, did not pick up taints from their surroundings. For a dry perry the practice was to let the juice complete its fermentation naturally and without interruption, whereas for sweet perries the fermentation process was usually controlled at the appropriate stage by the filtration of the liquor. The best farmhouse perries had the quality of high class white wines, and the connoisseur farmhouse makers produced both the dry and sweet perry.

The potency and quality of some of these old farmhouse vintage perries was apparently proverbial. A late eighteenth century Gloucestershire historian states that one of the Red Perries which he sampled was 'strong enough to flash in the fire'. A curious, but delightful testimonial to perry potency is furnished by the Gloucestershire poet W. R. Harvey. One of his dialect poems describes how a farmer, faced with the problem of transporting an intractable pig across the river Severn, drenched the porker with a good swig of perry which immediately put it to sleep. Much of its potency may be poetic licence, and, certainly, not all perries were as strong. Strong or not, in the eighteenth and nineteenth centuries, Gloucestershire perry, particularly that produced from a variety called 'Butt', was recognised as ideal for diluting wines and spirits and was, so we are told, widely bought for that purpose by wine importers in Bristol and London.

A marked characteristic of the perry pears, which go to make such a delightful and delicate drink, is the crude and unpleasant taste and texture of the raw fruit. The best cider apples are notoriously sour to the taste, but none has such an evil 'palate' as a small, stone-hard perry pear. The con-

The large number of different perry pear varieties produce fruit in all sizes, shapes and colours

trast between the gritty tongue-buckling raw fruit and the delicate winey drink it can produce has long been a source of astonished observation.

One perry propagandist, commenting on the contrast, wrote:

> though the juice of the perry pears is too harsh and rough as to occasion a long, continued heat and irritation in the throat when the fruit is attempted to be eaten: yet in the process of grinding it becomes rich and sweet without more roughness than is agreeable to almost every palate.

Scientific research shows that, as distinct from most cider apples, the juice of the perry pear is high in citric acid with a more complex amino acid and tannin structure. The colour of perry also reflects the differences in pear and apple composition. Perry is mostly of a pale straw tint, whereas ciders can vary from amber to red to brown, the different colours being due principally to the differential rates of oxidisation of their tannins during making.

Perry pears are also distinguished by diversity of names that must be unique in fruit growing anywhere in the world. The fact that fine perry can be made from the fruit of a single variety, and also that the same pear grown in different soils can produce perries of a radically different flavour and quality probably accounts, at least in part, for this extraordinary variety of names. Certainly the names of the perry pears make a register as rich and rabelaisian as the excesses that must have been committed under their influence. Some are synonyms for the same varieties growing in different parishes but, even so, the Gloucestershire list alone includes over 100 genuinely different varieties. The names variously reflect the parish of origin, the season of ripening, the breeder of the pear, the name of the farm or farmer, the shape or colour of the fruit. Often it is a comment on the quality of the perry which it produced.

There is obviously plenty of party spirit in the 'Merry Legs' of Blaisdon, East Dean and Stonehope, the 'Mad Pear' and 'Madcap' of Ashchurch and Saul (a name derived from the French 'saule' or 'willow'), the 'Huffcaps' of Hartbury, Newent and Taynton. More sinister and rueful, with perhaps groaning overtones of 'mornings after', are the 'Lumber' and 'Nailer' of Awre, and the 'Dead Boy' of East Dean.

Even less flattering judgements are implicit in the 'Stinking Bishop' and 'Bloody Bastard' of Churcham and Staunton, in 'Drunkers', 'Devil Drink' and 'Bastard Borland'. There are intimations of better things in the 'Brandy' of Micheldean, the 'Gin' of Rudford, the 'Port' of Dymock, the 'Claret' of Hendre Home Farm, the 'White Squash' of Corse and the 'Cowslip' and 'Late Treacle' of Newent.

Other names, even more curious because of their less obvious associ-

44

ations, are 'Snake Pole', 'Pig Pear', 'Clipper Dick', 'Grandfather Tum', 'Sickle Pear', 'Green Horse', 'White Bache', 'Ducks Barn', 'Hedgehog', and 'Pine'.

More specific in a roundabout sort of way is 'Circus Pear', (a name variant for the 'Blakeney Red' when grown in certain areas), so named because of the reputedly diuretic effect of this particular perry on the tipplers. Hence, drinking it meant 'one more round and out again' like the circus horse. Needing less explanation perhaps are 'Startlecock', 'Jug Rumbles' and 'Rumble Jumble'.

Traditionally, the perry pear tree with its zany directory of names has had another function apart from producing perry. Not surprisingly, in view of its striking appearance and its longevity, the perry pear tree has been planted for cosmetic as well as practical reasons. The 'Barland' variety was most often selected because of its commanding height, its graceful fold of limbs and its springtime plethora of large pink flowers. A magnificently decorative avenue of 'Barland' was planted near Much Marcle in Herefordshire to commemorate the coronation of Queen Anne; and, until recently, some of the original trees were still bearing fruit. There is also a superb procession of 'Barland' and 'Thorn' giants lining the approach to Boyce Court near the village of Dymock. These were planted during the latter half of the eighteenth century.

One tree in the Herefordshire village of Holme Lacy became a local legend. It was in its prime at the time of the French revolution when it was said to occupy over three quarters of an acre of orchard. In the course of a long life, the branches of the old tree, bowed by repeated loads of pears, had fallen and, as they rested wearily on the ground, natural layerings had taken place until the tree formed what was virtually a small orchard round the vestigeal central trunk. Some of the rooted branches were still to be seen on the site up to the 1950s. At one time this tree alone was reputed to yield seven tons of pears a year.

A considerable percentage of the present perry pear harvest used by the factory perry makers still comes from the old trees of Gloucestershire, Herefordshire, Monmouthshire and Worcestershire. (Worcester has 'three pears sable' in its coat of arms, added at the direct command of Elizabeth I when she visited the city, after, no doubt, she had drunk perry.) A few farms still produce the real farmhouse perry from the old trees in the old fashioned way.

A Ministry of Agriculture census of thirty years ago gave a return of approximately 75,000 trees, though many will have been grubbed out since that time. In defiance of tradition and in deference to progress, planting of the past two decades has taken place in Somerset, where the perry pear had

never previously been grown. These trees, in the hinterland of Shepton Mallet, supply the factory there, which produces what is now an internationally promoted beverage.

Down the years perry pears have had other uses than the making of perry. The famous 'Blakeney Red' of Blakeney is also widely used for stewing and bottling. The same variety is also reputed to have been raw material for the dye used in the manufacture of army khaki during the First World War.

The harvesting of these many different varieties of perry pears is a prolonged business and covers a period from the first week in September to the middle of November or later. Thus the great trees are a spectacular sight for the greater part of the year. Just as they greet the spring with their unique combination of majestic size and delicate, perfumed flowering so these old giants can signal just as memorably the arrival of autumn and the approach of winter. The towering trees of 'Red Horse', 'Red Huffcap' and 'Red Longdon', their leaf canopies tinged with autumn gold, their huge gnarled branches bowed with thousands of small blushing pears, kindle unforgettably in the red sunsets over the perry orchards of Awre, Lydney and Blaisdon.

(Opposite) Like a centenarian oak in flower, this tree of 'Blakeney Red' in springtime livery typifies the old perry pear giants

7 Fuller's Teasels

For two hundred years, Somerset teasels have been sent North by water, rail and road to the cloth-finishing factories of Yorkshire. The fuller's teasel (*Dispacus fullonum*), is the only agricultural plant which, virtually unprocessed and as harvested in the fields, is used as a tool in an industrial process. It is used in the cloth industry to raise the 'pile' or 'nap', and especially to produce the exquisite hard-wearing finishes known in the trade as 'doeskin' and 'beaver', and the flawless flat-pile finish demanded in specialist cloths like the coverings for billiard tables. Although fine wire brushes are now widely used in the nap-raising process, the fuller's teasel can still be the tool of choice for certain types of perfection finish. The key to the superiority of the teasel in this respect lies in the hundreds of tiny, hook-ended, downward-pointing awns which form in the seeded flower head.

A shrinking acreage of the fuller's teasel is still produced in the traditional teasel-growing area of South Somerset around the small country towns of North Curry, Curry Rivel, and Fivehead. Today, the fields have to be searched for, much more than even five years ago, but somewhere or other each year the crop is still to be found, throwing up the multi-branched stems, crowned with the purple and white flowers which mature into the prickly seed heads. The sight, a bizarre one to the casual passer-by, of twill-clad gatherers cutting what looks like a crop of seeded thistles is still to be seen.

The teasel is a biennial, and the heads which are eventually mounted in the gigs of the Northern cloth-finishing factories begin as handfuls of small seed sown in fine-tilth drills in the spring. Early field husbandry is like that for root crops, and the priority is to eliminate competing weeds.

By early autumn the plants have the appearance of large coarse lettuces and are ready for lifting with the special Somerset tool known as a 'spitter'. They are 'dibbled' – planted into holes made at regular intervals by a 'dibbling iron', which is a short length of stick with an iron point at one end and a cranked handle at the other. The plants are ranged along the ploughed furrows at a density of about 12,000 to the acre with about 24in between plants and 30in between rows. It is during this second year of growth that the teasel throws out the characteristic long central stem and numerous lateral branches. As the mauve and white flowers form and develop, the teasel fields buzz with activity. Teasel blooms are particularly attractive to bumble bees which seem immune to the mildly soporific effect which teasel flowers have on hive bees.

Traditionally teasel cutting in Somerset begins on August 1st. But it is

Teasel bunches are placed round the staff. They are then left to cure and dry in the wind

very much a prolonged, 'instalment' harvest with the crop being gone over several times, for teasel heads, even those on the same plant, ripen at different rates with days, sometimes weeks between. The largest heads are cut first, each individual being severed about 9in down the stem, with a small curved knife usually fashioned from old scythe blades. The knife is thonged to the strong leather gauntlet worn to afford protection against the tearing hooks of the seed heads. For the same reason, teasel harvesters always wear hard-surfaced clothes, commonly an old twill milking coat or a denim jacket.

As each teasel is cut, it is transferred to the other hand and the completed bunch is then thonged with a long teasel stem. The bunch, comprising 30 heads, is the primary unit of measurement. Given a clear day, one farmer in South Somerset who has produced some of the best teasels in post-war years could, in his prime, cut, bunch and toss into the various collecting points in the aisles up to 20,000 teasels. The enduring quality of his teasels is guaranteed by sowing seed from the most vigorous and prolific plants.

Once cut, the thonged bunches are collected from the aisles at the end of the day and assembled in circular fashion round 9ft long drying 'staffs'. Each bunch is pushed hard against the staff round which the heads close and cohere. A fully laden teasel totem traditionally holds 900 heads. When the weather is suitable, the teasel staffs remain outdoors, leaning against timber racks, so that the teasels can harden in the sun and wind. If the weather is damp, they are taken into open-ended sheds because the heads mould and soften rapidly if they are exposed, and so become unsaleable.

Traditionally, the Somerset teasel growers bunched their harvested heads in three categories – 'Kings', 'Middles' and 'Smalls' or 'Scrubs' – with the 'Middles' fetching the biggest prices. In recent years, all the grades have been bunched together although there is natural grading in that the big teasels are usually ready first and are thus harvested and bunched together.

In the autumn, when harvesting is ended, the teasel factor comes down from the North to tender for the teasels which are then bulked and railed to the Yorkshire cloth finishers in big canvas sheets or 'packs' containing up to 20,000 teasels.

Teasels have been used in the cloth factories in two ways, which varied according to region. In the Yorkshire 'teasel gig', the teasels are mounted in wooden frames which are fitted in turn on to the surface of a rotating cylinder. The cloth on which the 'nap' is to be raised is then counter-rotated against the revolving cylinder, so that teasels and cloth move against each other. In the West Country, the teasel gig was stationary and the cloth alone moved as it was drawn against the bracts. The use of teasels calls for a high degree of craftsmanship. Perfection of finish depends in particular on the judgement of the operator in the combination of new and old teasels and the optimum blend of 'Kings' and 'Smalls'.

This skill is particularly necessary with specialist cloths like the previously mentioned 'Beaver' and 'Doeskin'. The former has a thick woollen coating in twill weave with a deep nap finish resembling beaver fur, and the latter a cloth which is napped and felted for a perfectly smooth surface, and made in a satin weave of wool or worsted. These predominantly teasel finishes are achieved by what is known in the trade as 'wet raising', in the course of which the 'weave' of the cloth virtually disappears, and the trimmed pile eventually lies perfectly flat on the surface. 'Dry raising' is almost invariably done with fine wire brushes to produce a more pronounced pile in which the fibres stand up instead of lying flat, the finish of tennis balls being an extreme example.

From left to right, products of three stages in the use of teasel. The nap of the cloth is raised, then trimmed, and finally teaselled again. The result – trimmed, dyed billiard cloth

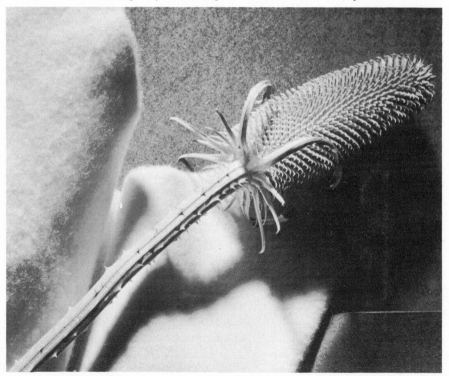

When the nap is raised, it has to be trimmed, which was formerly done with giant shears operated horizontally on the surface of the nap. The finest finish might involve teaselling and shearing the cloth up to thirty times. Cloth finishing was accepted as the most highly skilled of all cloth-making sequences, and, of these operations, nap-shearing of the teaselled cloth was recognised as the most skilled operation of them all. It remained so until the invention of the rotary nap-trimmer in 1815 by John Lewis, a cloth-maker of Stroud, who introduced a machine which cut the nap as a conventional lawn mower cuts grass. (The rotary lawn mower is in fact a technological 'spin-off' from the rotary nap-trimmer and was adapted from it, by another Stroud cloth manufacturer, later in the century.)

For the social historian, the teasel is of interest as an early focus and cause of industrial unrest in the English cloth industry. As early as the reign of Elizabeth I, a statute was in force forbidding the use of a rudimentary teasel gig which was designed to replace the old hand-operated teaselling frames. Despite attempts by Luddite-minded workers to get similar protective legislation passed, the finishing gigs made steady headway and, by the eighteenth century, Gloucestershire had become a centre of mechanised teasel-gig finishing for the West Country broadcloth. Some teasels were actually grown in Gloucestershire to service the industry and supplement the Somerset supply, but there has not been a teasel crop recorded in Gloucestershire since the early 1950s.

The cloth-making industries of Gloucestershire and Wiltshire are now much reduced, and broadcloth is largely superseded. Despite this, teasel-growing in Somerset continues, though teasels are increasingly thin on the ground. Soil and climate partly explain its survival, but the traditional market in the West Country cloth mills and in the North, and more especially, the tradition of cultivation, harvesting and marketing of a highly specialist regional crop are stronger reasons. Local pride and habit apart, the concrete reason for its survival today is the continuing market in Yorkshire for the diminishing supplies. Indeed reports of lapsed Somerset growers being asked to return to teasel cultivation by buyers from the North, may revive memories of fortunes made by growers in bygone days, and revitalise the industry.

A strong reason for the original establishment of the crop in Somerset may have been the suitability of the soil, and therein lies a curious tale of arable swings and roundabouts. The main bulk of the teasel crop has always been grown on the 'teart' soils of the county. These soils contain an excess of the trace element molybdenum, and cattle grazing on 'teart' pastures were notoriously prone to a serious and sometimes fatal wasting disease; an excessive molybdenum intake triggers a metabolic deficiency of copper in the cattle, which is the actual cause of debility. The problem is now dealt with by simply including copper sulphate in the cattle feed. However, until the relatively recent introduction of this panacea, the 'teart' farms were dependent on profitable cash crops, like teasels, to compensate for deficient dairy production.

During the middle part of the nineteenth century, when the West Country broadcloth industry was booming, some Somerset growers made fortunes from their teasels. In good years, the return from a crop exceeded the capital value of the land on which it had been grown. The dense-textured West Country broadcloth – it was woven on a wide or broad loom unlike the narrow fabrics – used up to 3,000 teasel heads on a 40yd roll of cloth. In view of this consumption, the cloth makers bought the teasels by the hundreds of thousand at a huge teasel mart held each autumn at Trowbridge in Wiltshire. In the best years, the standard pack of 900 teasels might fetch £20, and yields of up to 14 packs per acre were recorded.

The teasel is a notoriously gross feeder. Some old Somerset land agreements incorporated prohibitions against growing the crop for more than one year in seven, and occasionally specified a restriction of acreage as well. But some independent farmers, greedy for large profits, flogged their fields until they could literally grow teasels no more. The plants in their biennial year would not make the second-year transformation and instead bolted like seeding cabbages. With these exceptions, teasels traditionally fitted into a rotation in which they preceded wheat. They were seen as the ideal precursors of wheat, because their deep probing roots opened up and drained the subsoil. However, outside Somerset, they seem to have fitted into odd crop sequences. Arthur Young, the Georgian writer on agriculture, found them being cultivated in Essex in conjunction with the medicinal coriander and carraway grown for seed. Yorkshire also grew a small acreage near Huddersfield.

The first boost to the English growing of the bigger fuller's teasel coincided with the arrival of the technically advanced Flemish weavers in the sixteenth century. However, use of the teasel in a rudimentary cloth-finishing process dates from much earlier, conceivably from the arrival of the Romans, who introduced bigger sheep with better fleeces for making cloth. The first function of the teasel was probably the use of individual heads for 'carding' wool, the process of separating woollen fibres, prior to spinning. Carding teasels were certainly well known to the Romans, even before their invasion of Britain, for the word which describes the carding process is derived from 'cardus', the Latin term for thistle or teasel. Murals excavated at Pompeii show that, even then, the Romans were making use of the spiny teasel head to raise the nap on cloth, and the nap was trimmed to the required length by shears of a design borrowed probably from ancient Egypt. Today, one Somerset teasel grower is answering enquiries from Russia about his crop. So the Somerset teasel continues a long and picturesque tradition, and, after thousands of years, is still more than holding its own as an industrial tool.

8 Druggist's Herbs

LAVENDER

English lavender has the reputation of producing oil of the rarest quality. Acre for acre, the yield of English fields cannot compete with those of some Mediterranean growers, especially those in the Alpes Maritime, one of the principal lavender districts of Southern France. But, for bouquet and aroma, the oil from the English strain of the hybrid *Lavandula intermedia* is second to none.

Lavender has been grown in Britain for over three hundred years, and produce from the first cultivated beds put down at Mitcham in Surrey was soon nationally famous. The London cry – 'Buy my Lavender, sweet blooming Lavender' – invariably referred to the dried product of the renowned Mitcham beds. From Surrey, the blue aromatic fields spread into Kent and Hampshire, Suffolk and Herefordshire, Huntingdonshire, Essex and Lincolnshire and Norfolk. About twenty years ago, the Cistercians of Caldy Island, who had earned international renown for the quality of their perfumes sold from their own boutique in London, laid down some beds of white as well as blue-flowered lavender for use in their island still.

Precious crop products like essential oils are not infrequently associated with poorer soils, and this is certainly true of lavender. Like most oil bearing plants, lavender, which grows naturally in the Mediterranean countries, favours dry soils on sunny, fast draining slopes, often calcareous and stony in character, with a low rainfall and freedom from frost. Fertile land produces luxuriant vegetative growth and showy foliage, but fewer of the flowers in which the precious oil is concentrated. The precise natural function of aromatic oil can only be guessed at, but it is probably, at least in part, designed to increase the allure of flowers in the plant's wild habitat where pollinating insects are scarce.

Cultivated lavender is seldom, if ever, propagated from seed. Instead, young shoots, 6–9in long are dibbled in deeply, either 2ft apart or 18in on the square. With the latter planting pattern, the normal practice is to remove every second plant at the end of the first year for use as propagating material. This leaves the plants a yard apart with ample room for weed-shading lateral growth and flowering.

Growing lavender for oil is an exacting husbandry, for the beds must be kept scrupulously clean if maximum yields are to be obtained. The crop can be planted in either spring or autumn, and normally the bushes are kept from flowering in the first year in order to encourage bushy growth. Because the commercial plantation usually reaches the end of its economic life after five years, some producers follow the example of peppermint growers by planting 20 per cent of the target crop, repeating this each year until the target acreage is achieved. The first planting can then be grubbed in the fifth flowering year, without affecting the succession of crops coming into their prime.

The mature lavender bush is a handsome evergreen shrub, 1–3ft in height, its stem covered with a yellowish grey bark with flowers bluish violet or, in some varieties, white in colour. A field of lavender ready for harvest in late July or during August is a beautiful spectacle, especially when it is being grown for oil distillation, as the plants then have to be harvested in maximum bloom.

Growing lavender spikes for use as the traditional moth-repelling companion of bed linen or for inclusion in sachet or pot pourri, necessitates an earlier harvest than that for a distillation crop. In this case, the blooms are dried slowly, either in shaded places outdoors, or on trays in curing sheds. For sachets, the dried flowers are simply rubbed off, sifted of dust and bract residues and put in their tiny containers.

With oil crops, even the period of the day is critical for ensuring maxi-

A sample of lavender being prepared for distillation

mum yields of high quality. The best cutting hours are during fine, sunny mornings after the dew has vanished, or during warm evenings. Lavender fields are best left alone at high noon when the volatile, fruity essences of handled flowers dissipate easily in the heat. Either sheep shears or a sharp billhook are used to sever the flowering spikes together with about 6in of stem. After cutting the flowers are immediately taken to the still.

Modern lavender stills are usually made of copper, and can hold between 5–10cwt of flowers. The charge is placed on a perforated floor above a shallow space filled with water which is slowly steam heated to boiling point. Once the flow of oil from the heated lavender begins, it usually takes about six hours to complete the distillation. The other and older method is simply to boil the flowers in water. The oil-laden steam condenses in copper pipes, contained in cold water vats, and the oil is then separated and filtered. After distillation, the oil is stored and matured in the traditional 'Blue Winchesters' which used to be a familiar sight in the druggist's store. Yields vary greatly with the season and site, but a good acre of prime English lavender will yield 10–16lb of precious oil. Since lavender oil is also readily soluble in alcohol and lavender water, a solution of the oil in alcohol is another traditional English preparation from the distillation.

Today, lavender oil is used almost entirely for its perfume, but Gerard, the Cheshire herbalist, writing in his famous *Herbal*, speaks of conserves of lavender being served at table in England. This is not to dispute its status as a perfume. It is certainly one of the oldest of which we have knowledge; the Romans used it to sweeten their chaplets of flowers and their baths. Indeed, the name probably derives from the Latin *lavare* – to wash. A more venerable but less certain association is with St Mark. His 'spikenard' ointment was possibly a lavender unguent.

Lavender oil was also used medically, the usual dose being a few drops of oil taken with a little milk. Gerard recommends it as treatment for the palsy and Salmon in his *Herbal* makes the wider claim that, 'it is good against the bitings of serpents, mad dogs and other venomous creatures, being given inward and applied poulticewise to the part wounded. The spiritous tincture of the dried leaves or seeds, if prudently given, cures hysteric fits, though vehement and of long standing.'

Its reputation as a plague prophylactic made it a principal ingredient of the legendary Four Thieves Vinegar. The story goes that four Marseille thieves, their hands and faces covered in vinegar laced with spirits of lavender, rose and other herb essences, pillaged plague-infested houses with impunity. It has been used as a vermifuge in parts of France, and there is a dubious legend that big cats are rendered more manageable if they are sprinkled with oil of lavender.

OPIUM

The opium poppy (*Papaver somniferum*), which is commonly and misleadingly referred to as the White Poppy, grows in Britain in a number of colours: mauve, mauve and white, pink, lavender, purple and even blue, though this is a Tibetan variety still being experimentally grown. A common feature of most of these varieties is a spot, like a caste mark, on the base of the petals.

This exotic plant has been grown on a small scale in Britain for over a century. One curiosity in its brief British history is its concentration at one time near the village of Haxey in the Isle of Axholme. In this Lincolnshire village, it took an anomalous place in the anachronistic 'strip farming' that survived in that area until World War I. The poppy fitted into a rotation of turnips, potatoes and cereals.

Today, the opium poppy is more likely to be grown by the cereal growing farmer trying it as a 'break' between corn crops on the lighter lands; for, like lavender, the white poppy thrives best on calcareous soils with a light free draining texture. Its seed is tiny, with more than 50,000 to the ounce, and the crop is sown in shallow drills with about $2\frac{1}{2}$lb – roughly a million and a half seeds – to the acre. Sowing takes place towards the end of March, and the crop is ranged in rows sufficiently wide to allow mechanical thinning a month after plant emergence, the plants are finally singled to 5 inches apart.

The flowers begin to appear at the end of June and, by early July, the poppy field is a sea of wonderful blossom. Six to eight weeks after flowering, the poppy capsule begins to form. It is while the capsules are still green that they can be incised or pricked so that the white milky juice or latex exudes and coagulates on the surface. This is the opium which contains most of the alkaloids for which the white poppy is grown in the traditional opium-producing countries of Asia.

When poppy capsules are ripe, alkaloids are found in all parts of the plant other than the seeds. The seeds themselves, which may be white, yellow, blue, grey or black, are highly nutritious with more than 40 per cent of their weight in the form of high quality oil, and over 20 per cent in protein. Indeed, poppy-seed oil from cold, pressed poppies is comparable in quality with the oil of the olive. Because of its pleasant, nutty flavour the uncooked seed is also used in cakes and gateaux, or simply sprinkled on bread. In Britain, the crop is sold for seed pressing, the oil being used in the production of high quality artist paints and also as a hardening agent in plastic.

Opium-poppy capsules, which were once stocked by virtually every druggist, can still be bought over the counter in many chemist's shops. In earlier times deseeded poppy heads were widely used for fomentation poultices,

In ripe poppies, analgesic alkaloids are found in all parts of the plant other than the seeds

(the seed was sometimes sold as 'medicine' for canaries), though in some country districts the capsules were boiled, and the 'poppy tea' used as a pain-killing nostrum.

Before legislation created strict controls, opium itself could be easily bought in Britain. It came mainly as laudanum, a tincture of opium, which was drunk with water or wine and, in these days of prohibition, is now notorious. Crabbe, Keats, Coleridge, Francis Thompson, Elizabeth Barrett Browning, Wilkie Collins and Dickens were a few of the more famous adult users. An indication of its former currency is that even cough syrup and linctus were laced with laudanum. Dubious-sounding mixtures like 'Mother Bailey's Quieting Syrup' were typical of the laudanum-loaded specifics used on children in the nineteenth century. In view of our changed attitudes to opium products, it is perhaps surprising poppy heads are still available over the counter, for it is in the capsule that the poppy's alkaloid analgesics, morphine in particular, concentrate in greatest strength during ripening.

The traditional method of producing morphine is from opium, and opium production, though still based on peasant cultivation and harvesting methods which have hardly changed in 2000 years, has remained an essential part of morphine production. However, since the capsule walls actually contain morphine, recent experiments based on an English white poppy crop have provided most of the answers to the possibility that direct morphine production may be a commercial proposition.

Opium poppies were grown and intensively studied at Oxford University for twelve years, up until 1968. The object of the trials was to investigate the commercial possibilities of mechanised growing on British farms. The programme assumed that the seed would be sold for oil, while the capsule residues left after combine-harvesting, the poppy 'straw', would be used for the commercial extraction of alkaloids.

On the trial plots, yields of up to one ton of seeds per acre were obtained, though the plot performance was not repeated when the poppies were grown on a field scale. The principal difficulty was weed control, a problem which will no doubt be solved by the evolution of an effective herbicide which is not phyto-toxic to poppies. A more potent barrier was the unpredictability of English summers, for the ripening poppy crop demands continuously warm, dry conditions to ensure maximum yields of its constituents.

Despite these problems, the Oxford trials established certain important facts. Studies of ripening poppies showed that the best yields of seed, oil and protein are attained about five weeks after flowering, while the morphine content of the capsule reaches peak a few days later. It was also established that by varietal and individual culling or, in other words, by exploiting normal genetic selection, the morphine yield from the poppy capsules could be considerably increased.

Already the lessons of this English trial are being applied to the growing of opium poppies on the continent. Their work shows that direct extraction of morphine can yield seven to ten times more morphine per acre than the amount obtained in the traditional opium-producing areas. Largely as a result of the Oxford work with poppies, the production of opium to meet the world's medicinal need for poppy alkaloids could eventually become a thing of the past. However, the white poppy remains a vitally important plant, for *Papaver somniferum* is the only plant to synthesise morphine on a significant scale. As the synthesis of morphine in the laboratory is unlikely to prove economical in the foreseeable future, the white poppy provides the only large-scale source of this important analgesic alkaloid and its cultivation remains necessary in our world of pain.

PEPPERMINT AND HENBANE

Of the crops grown for medicinal and cosmetic purposes in Britain today, the biggest acreages are those of peppermint and henbane. Both are indigenous to Britain, and hundreds of tons of these attractive, interesting plants are harvested every year.

Peppermint has been cultivated commercially for well over a century. In 1850, 500 acres were under cultivation near Mitcham in Surrey, still one of the main centres of the industry. There are also substantial acreages in Hertfordshire, Cambridgeshire, Huntingdonshire and Lincoln. Like English lavender, English peppermint oil is judged to be the best in the world, for pungency and flavour.

The English oil is produced from both the white and the black peppermint plants (*Metha piperita var officinalis* and *Metha piperita var vulgaris*), but, although its oil is of finer quality, the white mint yields less, and the black mint is the most widely cultivated. It is a vigorous, ground-covering plant with finely serrated, dark, olive-green leaves and purple stems.

Peppermint is a sun lover and grows best on well-drained, calcareous land, provided the soil is deep enough. The crop is propagated from young plants grown from the 'runners'. These creeping roots are obtained from established beds. In March or April the plants are dibbled in on well manured, clean land at a rate of approximately 40,000 plants to the acre. They are kept scrupulously clean to ensure that no weeds – especially such polluting interlopers as cat mint, goose foot, corn mint or fat hen – find their way at harvest into the still. The crop is usually grown on raised 'lands' made wide enough to allow a trailer to be backed between the furrows for loading up at

A crop of black peppermint covers the field with a luxuriant carpet of dark green, glinting leaves

harvest. A vigorously growing crop of black peppermint soon covers the field with a rich luxuriant carpet of dark green glinting leaves.

The peppermint plant is ripe for cutting just before it begins to flower, which is usually in mid-August. As with the picking of hops, the peppermint harvest can be a hectic affair, but, unlike hops, some of the crop is still cut by hand, with small sickles known as 'mint-hooks'. Nevertheless, the bulk of the harvest is done with a mowing machine. If the peppermint is to be distilled in freshly cut condition, the rate of cutting has to be geared to the capacity of the stills which are kept working day and night.

Unlike some essential oil plants, however, peppermint can be partly cured and then distilled. In this method, the plants are laid to dry in long rows, turned like hay and then gathered into small heaps for final drying. They are afterwards bulked, wrapped in mats and stored for later delivery to the distillery. Well dried peppermint plants will keep for a long period. Peppermint is distilled in the same way as lavender, but, unlike lavender, the exhausted mint, after removal from the still, is always saved and carted back to the fields for use as manure.

The oil of the peppermint has a very slight yellowish tinge but thickens and assumes a reddish tint with age. Apart from use in confectionery, it has a number of medical applications and a widespread use as a flavouring to mask the taste of noxious medicines. The volatile oil of peppermint has great powers of penetration and is used, for example, in sanitary engineering where perfect sealing of joints must be absolutely ensured. The slightest imperfection in the seal is quickly betrayed by the peppermint in the testing steam or water.

The farm that grows peppermint will almost certainly be engaged in the cultivation of henbane (*Hyoscyamus niger*), one of the most valuable drug plants. It is of the same botanical order as tobacco and potato plants, and is sometimes found growing wild when it is easily identified by its sticky, grey-green leaves which are coarsely toothed and rough-textured, and its yellowish tubular flowers networked with purple veins. It is cultivated in two forms, the Annual and the Biennial. The leaves of both plants give off a strongly narcotic odour when squeezed, and both are important in modern medicine.

Uncertain germination and susceptibility to pests and fungi make henbane difficult to grow. Unlike many drug plants, it is drilled as seed in rows 2ft apart. Sowing takes place in the autumn, and the germinated seed produces seedlings in April or May, which are eventually singled to individual plants. In a good growing year, the large, pointed leaves, often a foot or more long, of the Biennial variety provide a first picking in July and perhaps a second picking again in September. This harvest yields the drug known officially as 'First Biennial Henbane'. Any leaves remaining then die back during the winter, and, during the second year, the big, flowering stem rises from the root crown to a height of three or four feet. This new growth is surrounded by a large rosette of hairy, pale green leaves, sticky with glandular secretions. This crop which is cut when the plants are in flower, yields the very valuable drug known officially as 'Second Biennial Henbane'. The Annual variety flowers during the first year and is usually ready for cutting in July or August.

The cut plants have to be dried without delay and are now mostly harvested with forage harvesters. Like its noxious counterpart, Belladonna, Henbane is the source of the important and highly poisonous alkaloid, hyoscyamine. It also produces hyoscine or scopolamine as this tranquilising, tension-relaxing drug is more widely known. The farm growing drug plants will almost invariably have small beds of a number of other species, grown not on a commercial scale, but to ensure that propagating material is available in case of a breakdown in imported supplies.'

One farm in the Eastern counties is typical in this respect. It had small areas of aconite whose root-tubers are the source of important alkaloids; roman chamomile which yields an essential oil; a special leafy strain of foxglove selected for its rich content of the glycosides used in treating heart disease; medicinal lettuce; lobelia which is used in the treatment of asthma; squirting cucumber – so called because, when the juice surrounding the seed in the small seed-gherkins swells to bursting point, the fruit ruptures and shoots the juice several yards – which yields the powerful cathartic, elatarium; and stramonium or thorn apple, whose alkaloids are used in asthma-relieving cigarettes. The farm also grew pennyroyal, marsh mallow, coriander, valerian and a number of other medicinal plants. Despite this apparent wealth, its stock is tiny compared with the 1600 different herbs reputedly grown in the 'Physic Gardens' of Tudor times.

Occupying a special place in the tradition of English medicinal plants is the liquorice of Yorkshire, a culture now virtually totally discontinued, though acreages were grown as late as the 1950s. These Yorkshire liquorice beds, principally in the Pontefract district, had existed without interruption since the time of Elizabeth I, when the crop was probably introduced into Yorkshire by the Black Friars. From Yorkshire, liquorice took root in Nottinghamshire, Surrey, where quite large acreages were grown near Godalming and Mitcham and also in Lincolnshire.

Liquorice has pronounced land preferences. The soil must above all be deep and good, and the old Pontefract beds, for example, offer the hungry root, for which the plant is grown, a light-loam topsoil that goes down stonelessly for many feet. The planting stock is cut from the crowns of lifted roots, and from the runners or rhizomes which, like those of bracken and peppermint, carry their own leaf buds. Liquorice matures into a handsome multi-branched shrub with light green, pinnate leaves, in the axils of which nestle the small, pale blue liquorice flowers. The roots are ready for lifting in the third season when both main roots and rhizomes are dug round and exposed for harvesting.

Formerly the famous Pontefract or Pomfret Cakes were always made from an extract produced from the freshly harvested English root, which supposedly has an exceptionally delicate flavour. But our homegrown labour-intensive crop has inevitably given way to cheaper peasant-harvested imports from the swamps of the Volga, where liquorice grows wild. Uncultivated liquorice is also found in Anatolia, Syria, and, even more romantic, in those parts of the Tigris and Euphrates valleys where the Garden of Eden was, by tradition, located. It is sobering to think how different the world might be if Eve had stuck to liquorice.

9 Cricket Bat Willows

Long-fibred, straight-grained, silky-textured, tough and, above all, light-weight, mature willow is the only possible wood for the cricket bat, itself one of the supreme instruments for translating strength and timing, gracefully and powerfully.

Norfolk, Suffolk, Essex and Sussex are the traditional home of the majestic, white-wooded bat willow (*Salix alba* 'Caerulea'), although they are also grown in the Home Counties, the Midlands, Somerset and, recently, on the west coast of Scotland. Some of the best trees of all grace the river basins of Essex and the lower Thames, where *Salix alba* finds the optimum blend of soil and climatic conditions: rich alluvial loam which the delicate roots can easily penetrate and probe for nutrients; good drainage with a moderately high water-table; adequate rainfall of about 35in a year, and days of leaf-nourishing summer sunshine for fast growth.

Willows flourish on the banks of rivers and streams, provided that the water is moving and well enough oxygenated to feed the mat of roots which they thrust greedily into the water. The quality of bat-willow timber is also critically dependent on the right soil, and *Salix alba* never produces good wood on peaty or gravelly soils or in waterlogged sites.

It takes from twelve to eighteen years to grow a good cricket bat. The trees are usually planted from January to March, either as poles cut from willows pollarded in the prime of life, or from specially raised sets both rooted and unrooted. The unrooted sets are mostly produced from low stools, as in the case of osiers, while rooted sets are taken from the shoots of three-year-old trees.

From the beginning of the tree's life, the grower has to guide its progress to coax the maximum yield of bats from each planting. The first requirement for a high-class cricket bat is wood with a straight grain. So the infant set must, above all, be straight and true because, in a crooked set, permanent wood curvature is already present. The stripling set should ideally be about 10ft tall, with an upright growth after planting of not less than 8ft. Because the best bat timber is contained in the lower bole of the tree, the aim, from planting onwards, is to ensure that the tree forms as much knotless and otherwise unblemished wood near ground level and up to the primary branches, as possible. To achieve this, the side shoots, which appear as the sets are being raised, are rubbed or pinched off while still young and tender. At this age, their removal makes no wound and leaves no scar. Once established in the right conditions, the bat willow comes on apace, being, apart from the poplar, the fastest growing of all English timber trees.

Like all fast growing trees, bat willows are voracious feeders and young trees are usually mulched to ensure quick establishment and guard against possible drought. Any buds which appear on the precious bole during the first three or four years are, again, carefully rubbed off with hand protected by a hedging-glove to a minimum height of 8ft. The sweet green rind so much loved by grazing animals has also to be protected against the damage of teeth, as well as itchy rumps.

With the main bole clean and clear of side branches up to a height of 8–10ft – growers speak of a three-or four-bat bole depending on the height of the primary branches – the bat willow soon begins to form the spectacular crown which makes it such a toweringly graceful adornment. Its appearance is one of the advantages of rapid maturing. Fast, uninterrupted growth is always associated with a big spread of green leaf ensuring efficient photosynthesis. The formation of the crown and canopy is promoted by generous planting distances between trees. Because of this need for maximum light and air, bat willows are hardly ever grown in woodland form.

A *Salix alba*, towering above the river, is, undeniably, a compelling sight. The clean straight bole with its grey, patterned bark, vaguely reminiscent of lizard skin, is dominated by the great feeding apparatus of branches and leaves mirrored in the flowing water. The sun gives a glowing translucency to the bluish grey leaves. As the breeze catches them, they flirt their silvery undersides making the whole tree shimmer. Where they are planted for amenity purposes, and are allowed to go on growing, these giants will reach a height of 100ft and more.

As a general rule, the bat tree is ready for felling when it has a quarter girth of about 11in at a height of 5ft. On well drained sites rich in organic nutrients, this usually takes 12–16 years, although in exceptional circumstances like the silty banks of flowing streams, trees can be ready for felling a decade after planting. However, too rapid growth is not desirable, and bat makers regard the laying down of two growth rings a year as the optimum rate of growth. At that rate, the tree takes about fifteen years to become suitably mature.

Felling the bat willow is a skilled operation, for the tree must fall cleanly. The usual method involves digging round the trunk to expose the spur roots and sawing as near the ground as possible. After the first cut, a second is made opposite and slightly above the first incision. As the saw bites in and the second cut deepens, the tree tilts and closes the first cut. With the use of wedges and after a series of sideways cuts, the final core of tree is cut through.

(Opposite) This plantation of bat willows shows the wide spacing which encourages the graceful, airy crown and canopy essential for fast growth

The bat-willow grower does not have to wait long to measure his success in the number of high-quality bat lengths or 'clefts' which the branchless bole will yield. As soon as the tree is felled, lopped and topped, it is delivered to the bat-maker and the willow logs are sawn into sections known as 'rounds', 'bolts' – the term used also to describe the standard bundles of osiers and rushes – or 'rolls', each 28in in length.

These rolls are then split into clefts, a skilled task which is performed with a wedge or axe, and beetle or heavy mallet, the rolls being split along the radial lines which, plainly seen on the outer circumference of the roll, indicate where the wood should be split. The rolls must always be split in such a way that the annual rings run from the front to the back of the bat. If the wood were cut so that the rings ran the other way, the bat would not stand up to the jarring impact of the ball.

The sapwood of a well grown willow log is virtually white, while the heartwood nearer the centre has a reddish brown tinge. The last wood to be formed, that of the last annual growth ring, is not normally good enough for bat making and is usually removed before the seasoning of the clefts begins. A sound fast-grown tree of 11in quarter girth should furnish eight clefts from each round.

With the bark removed, the clefts are then roughly shaped into isosceles triangles, $4\frac{1}{2}$in at the base, carefully stacked in threes with plenty of air space between, and left seasoning out of doors for one entire year. They are then brought into sheds where they are air-dried and seasoned for a further three months. Whereas the weight of the freshly felled bat willow is approximately 44lb per cu ft it weighs only 21 to 26lb per cu ft after seasoning and drying.

So from 12–16 years after planting, the seasoned clefts pass into the hands of the bat-making craftsman. Although bat making, like most traditional wood crafts, has entered the age of technology and many of the bat workshops are mechanised, some of the best bats are still made by hand.

For the traditional craftsman, the first task is to trim the roughly hewn cleft into bat shape. This is done to an oversize measurement, with the face and sides left thicker than the intended size of the bat. The reason for this is that, although pristine willow wood combines resilience and toughness to a remarkable degree and is able to sustain a substantial amount of shock without splintering, the wood of the cleft is not yet in a condition to stand up to repeated punishment from a hard ball which may strike the wood at seventy miles an hour. To strengthen and harden it, the oversize cleft undergoes, with periodic rests, a process of progressively increasing compression between spring-loaded rollers.

The wood of the bat willow has the ideal density for improving under pressure and this attribute above all others makes it the perfect bat wood. Wood that is too soft, compresses too much and too easily and may splinter, while intrinsically hard wood is too heavy. *Salix alba* alone combines strength, softness and resilience for the compression demanded by the bat-maker.

In some small bat-making workshops, even the process of rolling may be done by hand by craftsmen who are loath to lose touch with the material at any stage. If, after compression, the fibres are judged to need just a little more compression, the bat-maker will apply the final touches by hand with a specially-faced mallet. He then cuts the slot for the bat handle, and the handle itself, made up of square sections of cane glued together, is spliced into the bat, bonding in so tightly that even before glueing it is almost impossible to pull it out.

The final shaping of the bat with its sloping shoulders, swelling middle and curving edges and base is always done by hand, even in the mechanised workshops where power-driven saws and rollers, and revolving shaping-knives are the order of the day. For the final finish of the top-quality cricket bat, there is no substitute for the balancing hand and eye of the long-experienced craftsman using the tools of his trade.

Draw knives and spokeshaves are honed razor-blade sharp to enable the bat-maker to wafer-shave the wood. Such delicacy is essential if he is to achieve the exquisite balance which is vital. Balancing the bat, like tuning a bell, is the most skilful part of the craft – a continual judgement of shaving, smoothing fingers and hefting palm. The bat is then lightly sandpapered, polished and stamp-inscribed with the legend of maker and sponsor. The finished product weighs from 2lb 2oz to 2lb 7oz.

Our cricket bats have changed surprisingly little in the last hundred years. Indeed, it can be fairly said that the cricket bat of today dates from as far back as 1771. In that year, a cricket match between Hambledon and Chertsey for a wager of £60 a side saw one player, White by name only, address the ball with a bat so wide as to defy being beaten. To forestall further caddish deviations, a statutory width of $4\frac{3}{4}$in for club cricket bats was proposed.

Fittingly, Britain remains the only cricket bat manufacturer of any consequence, and our native bat willow has no rival. Current demand runs at about 14,000 mature trees a year, which means that, taking in all stages of growth and ages of tree, we need up to 300,000 trees in cultivation at any one time. Actually the commercial cultivation of *Salix alba* for bat-making dates only from about the beginning of the present century. Until then, cricket bats were made from the thousands of trees which had sprung up along the rivers and watercourses of the Eastern counties, as a result, mainly, of adventitious rooting of willow poles and sets put into the ground for fencing and other purposes. Before planting eased the supply problem, bat-makers at the turn of the century sent their scouts out each autumn to hunt the country for suitable trees. This demand drove them farther and farther afield as the East Anglian bat timber became exhausted, until few trees remained except for those planted in parks and round stately homes. When the first big planting took place around 1905, growers were paid approximately five shillings per foot of useable tree.

The cricket bat willow undoubtedly provides the best timber of any of the willow species. Its unique combination of toughness, freedom from taint and resinous or other secretions, and its easy working when seasoned makes it suitable for a wide variety of purposes. Apart from cricket bats, its lightness and strength make it particularly valued for the making of artificial limbs. The strength of association, however, is well illustrated by the story of the artificial leg made for the poet, W. H. Davis. This was invoiced to his friend, Edward Thomas, by the puzzled village wheelwright as 'Curiosity Cricket Bat'. Its lightness and resistance to splintering – it tends to dent rather than split under hard impact – also make it ideal for skittle and polo balls, as well as balls for coconut shies. It is also used for knife boards, saddle-trees and toys.

The ease with which most species of seasoned willow can be shaved into wafer-thin ribbons, makes willow first-choice wood for light non-returnable receptacles such as punnets and other 'chip' baskets, used mainly for holding fruit. Formerly a rural craft, particularly in the soft fruit growing districts of the West Country and the West Midlands, the making of these woven containers is now a combined operation of machine and hand labour. The long strips of willow are sliced off by machine, but the fine criss-cross weaving of the punnet is still done by hand. The punnet is actually a much simplified cousin of the 'trug', the name formerly given to an old English measurement for wheat. The trug is a strong basket of willow ribbon, fashioned round a framework of cleft chestnut, and traditionally associated with Sussex.

Willow wood is also used for brooms and brush-heads and the floors of waggons and lorries. Although the primary branches of the cricket bat willow previously went for burning, they are now sold for the making of pulp destined for use in the manufacture of fibre-board and paper.

10 Basket Osiers

The basket willow, osier or withy (*Salix triandra*), like the fuller's teasel, is closely associated with Somerset, for that county grows more than three-quarters of the British acreage. Soil and climate are the main reasons for this almost complete monopoly of production. The confluence of four Somerset rivers, the Tone, the Parret, the Yeo and the Isle provide growing conditions which are uniquely favourable for their cultivation.

Paradoxically, the moisture-loving osier thrives best in an environment of low rainfall and long, hot summers. The river-bounded Somerset moors, with the little village of Burrowbridge at their centre, provide exactly this blend of conditions. The plains are girdled by hills which take most of the water out of the clouds, so that the rain-shadowed osier beds receive an annual rainfall which seldom exceeds an optimum 28in. But, because the moors, with their tidal rivers, are mostly at sea level or only a little above it, the water-table in the soil is often at the surface, and, even in droughty summers, rarely falls below 18in. This ensures the roots of the osier a constant supply of moisture.

This unusual combination of hot, dry summers, low rainfall and high water-table is matched by soil conditions which are nearly perfect. The Somerset osier-growing soils are deeply fertile, consisting of clay and alluvial deposits overlying well humified peat, which is very rich in organic matter – sometimes up to 50 per cent – and has a high natural phosphate content. This high fertility is maintained by the winter-flooding rivers which may lay an inch a year of rich riverine silt over the willow beds. It is, no doubt, this flooding – less frequent with the development of large, local drainage schemes – which produces the erroneous impression that these Somerset moors are areas of high rainfall. This part of Somerset also enjoys a mild winter, so the standing water of pit and ditch in which osiers are kept during the winter seldom freezes and the grower can get on with his processing in the winter months.

Basket osiers are produced as annual coppice shoots from permanent stools, and the beds are grown in long-term rotation with grass. Virgin land is ploughed in the autumn and then left for the kneading fingers of frost to break down and crumble. In spring, the ploughed field is harrowed and cultivated repeatedly to produce a clean, friable tilth. The 12in cuttings known locally as 'drawn withies' are then planted by hand in rows 24–27in apart, giving about 17,000 stools to the acre.

Clean land is the top priority, and the use of modern residual herbicides has been a boon for osier growers. Despite this, weed control, particularly in

In summer and autumn, Burrowbridge, a centre of osier growing, is hedged about with thousands of drying canes

the early stages, remains a constant battle. The warm, humid growing conditions, which suit the osier are also ideal for weeds. These, if not adequately treated, can form thick mats which shade and stunt the young growing shoots.

The biggest weeds, particularly meadow sweet, comfrey, docks, bindweed and bramble, compete for moisture and nutrients with the young set which has to develop both shoots and roots from the food supplies available. But, by the fifth to seventh year, the osier is established with fully developed roots branching widely to probe and plunder the rich soil.

While chemical herbicides are used in the preparation of new beds, they are not so effective in the established plantations, for the osier is highly sensitive to many of the most effective herbicides. Although the Willow Officer at the Long Ashton Research Station, University of Bristol, working in co-operation with the progressive growers, resolved most of the husbandry difficulties of the osier craft crop, the fight against weeds is still laborious. The hand hoe, together with some remarkable 'Heath-Robinson' cultivators, usually cannibalised and adapted from a combination of machines, is still very much in use. The osier grower has to be adept at engineering improvisations, for there are no standard machines to meet his special requirements. The remotely sited osier beds produce a hardy, independent and resourceful mixture of individualist husbandry man and engineer.

Osiers cannot compete with the hops for speed of growth but, even so, on days of high summer the canes can lengthen by up to an inch in twenty-four hours. This rapid, uninterrupted growth is needed to ensure the long, straight canes which command the best prices. Fast growth is vital also to take the growing osier safely through its annual period of insect attack, particularly from the willow beetle. The key to a straight skywards-straining osier is to keep the apical growing point undisturbed and undamaged. The cane does not then develop sideshoots which, as with the cricket bat willow, would ruin its value. To prevent this, the osiers are sprayed several times a year against pests.

A thriving plantation of healthy osiers can last for half a century and, in a good year, each stool can yield 15–20 rods, making an approximate total of 300,000 rods or about 5 tons of fresh weight per acre. These figures underline the laborious nature of the harvest, for most of the crop is still cut by hand, and each acre will take an experienced cutter eight days. The rods have to be severed close to the stool and the harvest is difficult to mechanise successfully. Machines can be moderately effective under ideal conditions, when the beds are free of weed and the stools, small, of a standard size, and close to the ground; but such conditions are extremely rare.

Although the maiden osier is cut in its first year, the initial crop is often crooked and unmarketable so it is cut largely to build up the root system for future yields. The winter harvesting of the osiers begins when the frosts have begun to thin out the leaves. Each individual rod is obliquely sliced from the stool with a sickle. The rods are gathered and tied with osier canes, in bundles or 'bolts' which have a circumference of 37in at a point 2in from the base, and weigh about 27lb. The tallest rods, after a good growing season, may measure up to 10ft in length, but the dominant rods are more likely to measure 6–7ft, and the average $4\frac{1}{2}$–5ft.

Today, the osier crop is hauled home with tractor and trailer, but, in the days of frequent flooding, the flat-bottomed Somerset 'withy boat' was a familiar sight. Laden to the gunwales with 'bolts', it was poled home down the overflowing 'rhines' as the main water courses are known. Now, the installation of pumping stations on the Somerset levels and the complex interlinkage of rhines and ditches not only reduces flooding, but also enables the waterways to be used for irrigation, so maintaining the high water-table in which the osiers thrive.

The growing and harvesting of the osiers is only the first stage of the lengthy journey to market, however. The exceptions are the freshly cut or 'green' osiers, which, after steaming, are allowed to dry out and are sold unpeeled as 'browns'. These are the cheapest form of osier, and not many are sold in this category. The aristocrat of the osier beds is the white peeled rod, which is produced in two ways. There is a short spring period, as the cambium or cellular tissue of the osier is beginning to divide, when the bark peels easily. So a number of the stools are left unharvested over the winter and cut in the spring as the rind-loosening sap begins to rise. This is known as 'whitening off the stocks', and, during this short period, the osiers are cut and peeled to provide a gleaming white finish. However, the number of rods which can be produced in this way is relatively small. The osiers will only peel for the relatively brief period before the new wood begins to form, after which the detachable rind joins on to the new wood.

Thus the bulk of the white rods are produced from winter-harvested osiers kept alive in the water of ponds, ditches and shallow concrete tanks. In the spring, the unpeeled dormant rods begin to sprout again. But, unlike the growing canes left on the stools for whitening off the stocks, the pitted osiers do not produce new wood, and the period during which they can be peeled for 'whites' extends through into July.

Stripping the osier by the traditional method of drawing the osier through a simple 'break' of iron

The other principal osier category is the 'buff'. Buffing transformed the osier grower's routine by making it possible to peel and process right through the year, instead of just during a short period in the spring. The process was discovered in Nottinghamshire in the mid-nineteenth century. It was found that, after several hours boiling in an open tank, the osiers could be easily peeled, and that, at the same time, the boiling process imparted an attractive, reddish brown stain to the rods. The buff colour derives from the decomposition products released during boiling, but its richness depends on the osiers being grown in the right kind of clay soil, and boiled osiers off peatlands, for example, remain a pale anaemic colour.

Peeling or stripping the willow is a combination of old and new techniques. Today, it is mostly mechanised, the osiers being peeled in bundles held against rotating drums, but hand stripping does still survive. By this method, the osier is pulled through a 'break', a piece of sharpened hoop iron shaped like the letter 'Y', set at an easy working height on a post or fence. Machine peeling, however, is at least ten times as fast as the hand operation.

The old and the new exist side by side in the osier country because there are a number of small growers who combine part-time cultivation of an acre or two of willows with another job. For them mechanisation would not be economical and many sell their osiers as a standing crop to be cut and processed by the purchaser. Some market small consignments of processed rods to bigger growers who wish to supplement their stocks.

Over the years, the industry has suffered much from foreign competition, which took advantage of the fragmented unorganised structure of the British industry. However, osier growers are now organised as a special branch of the National Farmers' Union and marketing schemes have been negotiated with principal buyers. Today, ten acres of willow will provide a good, if hard, living for a Somerset osier grower and his family, although many now combine osier growing with dairy farming and cider apple production.

British osier growing, like perry and cider making, received its first big boost from the Napoleonic wars which interrupted the imports of osiers and baskets from France. The isolationism encouraged, indeed enforced, by the Napoleonic wars also coincided with the first major drainage of the Somerset flats which made tracts of land, highly fertile but still subject to flooding, available for a suitable crop. The osier was a natural choice for exploiting such land and, apart from Somerset, acreages were also established in Nottinghamshire, the Cambridgeshire fens, and also in Essex, where the crop is still grown on a small scale.

A developing fashion for basket furniture brought a minor boom to the British osier industry which reached its apogee in the early 1900s. At that

Baskets for cats and the GPO. With square and rectangular baskets, the upright canes are fixed first and the rods woven in between

time, large numbers of villages had their own basket-maker – some Somerset villages still do – turning out furniture and standard containers for domestic and trade purpose, as well as producing bespoke designs.

Basket-making is one of the most ancient methods of making receptacles because, in their crudest form, baskets can be produced literally without tools. Nor has it been possible, or perhaps worthwhile, to mechanise the process in modern times. So it remains a craft, much of it now concentrated in the factories of the blind. It is very much a skill of touch which can fairly readily be taught. Blind basket-makers work on a floorboard with the minimum of simple tools: a pair of basket secateurs or shears; a sharp knife ('shop knife'); a bodkin, much like a bradawl, to make openings for the rods and a pair of bull-nosed pliers to pull the rods through the weave. Apart from the usual knives, cleavers, planes and probes, the basket-maker makes use of what is surely the most resoundingly named tool of any trade. This is the 'commander', or ring-ended iron rod, with which he beats and shapes the weave of the growing basket.

Though it has a multitude of different forms and functions, the basket is still of course the prime osier product: baskets for cats and dogs, laundry and mail, textiles and theatre props, fruit and vegetables, feed and seed, pigeons and wine bottles, chickens and ducks, malt and dung, shopping and picnics. The fish trade uses a basket unit of measurement, and tens of thousands of 'crans', 'prickles', 'swills', 'flats' and 'creels' are in use in various fish ports. Osier receptacles are widely used by potato growers, by Covent Garden porters, for carrying clay in the Potteries and peat in the Irish bogs. Osier lobster pots apparently still last longer than those of any other material, and no better alternative has been found either for the framework round which the Guardsman's 'bearskin' is constructed.

Apart from the competition of foreign imports, the British osier, like most natural products, has had to face the challenge of man-made materials and in particular the challenge of the non-returnable container. However, this is a diminishing practice in a suddenly conservation conscious world. On balance, the osier has more than held its own as a popular material for domestic and industrial containers. It offers a unique combination of durability, lightness, strength and an attractive appearance. Having weathered the assault of the plastics, demand and supply are at last fairly evenly balanced.

The historic osier-growing moors of Somerset remain picturesque and remote. The legions of drying canes, leaning against walls and fences, hedgerows and sheds, appear with almost dramatic suddenness as one travels across the county. The people are as caught up with the crop as they ever were. Their speech is still peppered with the terms of the growers' and craftsmans' vocabulary. Varieties like 'Black Maul' and 'Brown Spaniard,' 'Glibskins' and 'Dicky Meadows', 'Champion Rod' and 'Pomeranian' are bandied about. In pubs, people discuss 'buffs', 'browns', 'whites', 'drawn withies', 'whitening off the stocks'. The remaining local basket-makers, now a diminishing species in the actual growing areas, speak of 'randing', the simple in-and-out weaving of a single rod through the uprights; 'slewing', the same process with two or more rods and 'waling', an operation in which three or more rods are worked alternately for an extra stout weave. Today the osier and those associated with it remain unruffled by the winds of changes, which, if anything, are blowing their way again.

11 Fisherman's Willow

In no part of Britain has basket-making remained a more unchanging and vital craft than on the lower reaches of the Severn estuary. For perhaps a thousand years, the willow and the hazel have joined together in tough, pliant, water-resisting partnership to produce the unique baskets – those 'fixed engines', virtually unaltered over the centuries – with which the fishermen sift the waters of the estuary.

Severn fishermen have recorded many interlopers in these baskets including porpoise, shark, sturgeon, giant congers and the sea-lampreys, those weird living fossils eaten to excess by English kings and queens almost since Norman times. However, despite these diverting intrusions, the craft of the Severnside basket-maker is principally associated with the trapping of salmon from the opaque, heavily silted tidal waters.

It is, of course, basket-making with a difference. These containers are unique to the River Severn, and none more so than the 'kipe', a giant fish trap loosely woven in hazel and osier round a score of strong, 7ft hazel staves. The kipe, which gives its name to the completed basket, is strictly the first of three sections which go to complete this most ingenious of fish traps. To this big bell-shaped, hazel kipe with its mouth diameter of 8ft is joined the 4ft long osier 'butt', a secondary basket of finer weave, to which is attached in turn the open-ended, finely woven, osier 'foreweel'. This tapers down to a few inches at the end which, once the basket is in the river, is usually stoppered with seaweed. The foreweel contains a 'chale' of pointed hazel, which functions as a one-way 'valve', and makes escape impossible.

These giants of hazel and osier are usually dragged into place in the estuary by horse and sled, but have to be manhandled for the final slithering stage of the haul across the Severn mud. Many kipes are sited far out in the estuary, facing up stream. Fastened to strong, wooden stakes grouted into the rock of the river bed, with 'rods and pins' fashioned out of osier and hazel, the entire installation is an immensely strong, woven conglomerate locked together without benefit of nail or screw. The completed fishery, or 'weir', of kipes may incorporate up to a hundred baskets which are washed through by the roaring river twice in every twenty-four hours.

In position, the kipe bears a striking resemblance to the physical conformation of the estuary itself. The river is wide at the mouth and has bottleneck upper reaches which are the spawning destination of the gravid salmon. The kipe fisheries are made more effective by blind basket-work 'hedges' of loosely woven hazel which extend a hundred yards or more on either side of the weir.

This fine salmon has been scuppered by the 'road-of-no-return' engineering of the kipe

Many of the Severn salmon which find their way on to the slabs of the fishmongers in Bristol and the Midlands are caught on the ebb tide. The fish, blindly seeking a way upstream in the fast-flowing, muddy water, encounters the wicker hedge and swims along its length looking for a way out, until it finds one – in the yawning mouth of the kipe. It continues swimming forward, only to become trapped in the butt, and, being like any fish, unable to swim backwards, it is buffeted forward by the fast-flowing tide. In the stoppered foreweel, the salmon may join other, smaller fish brought in by the tide, such as twait, allis shad, shrimps, whiting and eels.

Between tides, by day or night, the fishermen slog across the viciously-clinging mud to inspect the kipes, and bring home any catch in shoulder-slung baskets or 'witchers'. The principal danger to the catch is mutilation by marauding gulls and crows, the main hazard to the fishermen comes from the engulfing tide which can return with the speed of a galloping horse. At the end of the season which extends from April to August, the foreweels are removed from the kipes so that the spawned salmon or 'kilts' can return to the ocean after spawning, as can also the small salmon 'parr', the young fish coming downstream on their ocean migration. Battered by storms and even, in rare winters, by icefloes, the Severn kipes rarely last for more than three or four seasons. Replacing them is a long, laborious winter's task for the fisherman-cum-craftsman.

The kipe filters the tide of swimming things with the precision almost of a

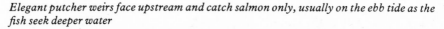

Elegant putcher weirs face upstream and catch salmon only, usually on the ebb tide as the fish seek deeper water

baleen whale. The second product of the Severn basket-maker, the 'putcher' or 'putcheon', on the other hand, is so constructed as to trap only salmon or other large fish. Like the kipe but not so closely woven, it is fashioned round a series of hazel staves, with a trio of discs or girdles of osier forming a wicker funnel, 5½ft long and 30in wide at the mouth but tapering to 2in at the butt.

While the kipe weir may, exceptionally, number a hundred or more baskets, in excess of fifteen hundred putchers may be assembled in weirs, with the elevated baskets in ranks up to 10ft in height. The putcher weirs either extend into the estuary from the river bank, or are attached like kipes to frameworks grouted on the river bed. Half the traps on a putcheon weir may be set facing upstream, and half the other way so as to exploit both tides. Like all osier artefacts, the putchers are extremely light as well as very strong, and so are carried into position on the fisherman's back, packed one inside the other like ice-cream cones. Unlike the kipes, they are brought home when the season ends in August.

Apart from a few putchers borrowed for use in the nearby Wye, the salmon putchers and kipes of Severn are found nowhere else in Britain. Just as confined in its use is the lave-net, which is perhaps an even more distinctive and unique example of the craft and skill of the Severn salmon fisherman. Its design and materials, theoretically at any rate, may be unchanged since prehistoric times, and, with it in his hands, the fisherman becomes once more a hunter rather than a harvester.

The lave-net consists, basically, of a wooden Y-shaped frame over which the 4in mesh net is strung. The arms of the 'Y', the 'rimes', which are 6ft long, are bolted to each other where they cross, a few inches below the end of the handle or handstaff. The rimes are in turn bolted to the 'yoke-board', a narrow rectangular piece of wood, attached at right angles to the handstaff. The right-hand rime is ingeniously removable, allowing the lave-net to be folded up for carrying.

Fishermen invariably make their own lave-nets, and a fetish is made of selecting the perfect piece of growing ash for the handstaff, which must possess a natural 'crank' – rather like that of the steamed ash scythe handle – at a point 6in below the yokeboard. This allows for comfortable portage on the shoulder when the net is folded. Whereas the handstaff is always of ash, the rimes are invariably of willow, chosen for its lightness, resilience and strength. These attributes are, together with perfect balance in the finished article, the principal requirements of a hunting instrument with which the fisherman has to sprint and scoop the powerful salmon out of the water as it swims desperately hither and thither to escape from the shallow tidal pools. The vigilant lave-net fisherman is first alerted to its presence by the tell-tale

The Severn lave-net is used to catch salmon stranded in pools at low tide. Its use demands skill, speed, strength and knowledge of the estuary

wake or 'loom' which it produces on the pool surface.

The lave-net fisherman has always enjoyed primal status among the craftsmen of salmon-catching Severnside, for laving is usually a skill handed down through the family. It demands a good eye, the timing born of long experience, physical strength, great speed, intimate knowledge of the riverbed and close understanding of the instinctive behaviour of the fleeing salmon. When the salmon charges into the strategically placed lave-net, the fisherman must lift the violently struggling fish out of the water, ground the handstaff and, in a matter of seconds, draw his lead-loaded cosh – variously known as the 'priest', 'molly knocker' or 'knobbling pin' – to kill the leaping catch.

There are tales of monsters that have got away by breaking through the lave-net mesh, but salmon weighing up to half a hundredweight have been successfully landed. Traditionally, kipe and putcher weirs are, if possible, sited where sand and shallows form pools between the tides. In this way, lave-net catches can supplement the often scanty or non-existent produce of the baskets. But not all kipe and putcher sites have the sandy bars and tidal pools necessary for lave-net fishing, nor are all salmon fishermen licensed to use the lave-net. If they are not the owners, salmon fishermen pay rent for their sites to the owners, rates to the local authority and licence money to the Severn Water Board.

The same Severnside skills which produce the lave-net and salmon baskets were once also employed in the weaving of exquisite urn-shaped wicker containers known as 'hard wheels' or 'cunning kipes'. These were used for keeping lampreys alive in the river. The storage baskets were tethered to stakes, and the immersed lampreys could be kept alive for considerable periods, until extracted for the, often regal, table.

Even more graceful and pleasing to the eye is the eel trap of the River Severn. This is woven out of withy, and braided into an open-ended shape resembling a wine bottle with a swollen belly. The wide end is for the eels to enter, and the narrow end is simply plugged to hold the bait – reputedly the eel's favourites are rabbit and lamprey – and allow the captured eels to be removed. The interior of the trap is ingeniously equipped with two constricted throats of springy cane pointing towards the narrow end. These act as one-way valves and are called 'chales', which permit the eels to pass through into the trap but then close behind them and prevent their return. These eel traps are tethered in the river, mostly facing upstream, to attract the sexually mature 'silver' eels as they move down-stream in their nuptial livery to begin migration to the Sargasso Sea, where they spawn and die.

Any eels which run the gauntlet downstream will previously have escaped the distinctive nets of the Severn eleverers, when they moved upstream anything from five to twelve years before. As with the lave-net, the Severn elver fishermen make their own nets and the design is unique to the estuary. The handle, or 'tailstick', of the elver net is 7–9ft long and is usually fashioned from elm. Also of elm is the wooden part of the semi-circular or triangular headboard through which the handle passes. The wooden side-stick strainers are made of withy, and the framework is rigidly strung with about a yard and a half of the strong cheese-cloth, which was once widely used to wrap cheese in the Double Gloucester dairies of the Severn Vale. The whole forms an open, box-shaped sieve of a pleasing shape through which the river water drains, and in which the elvers remain.

Elvers mean many things to the inhabitants of the riverside villages. They are a crop, a craft, a cult of unholy hours. They mean wet and sometimes freezing vigils, the competitive cameraderie of moonlit nights and, of course, hard cash. From mid-February until the end of April, news of the approaching hosts runs like a grapevine through the bars of the riverside inns. One recognises the elverer from the way he consults his watch, mind-mapping the progress of the racing tide past Oldbury, Shepherdine, Berkeley, Sharpness, Purton, Frampton-on-Severn, Framilode, Epney, Longney, Wainlode Hill, Apperley, Deerhurst and on to the great weir at Tewkesbury. Half an hour before the catch is due at the selected vantage point, the elverers shoulder long-handled nets and move in the gathering gloom to the pewter-coloured river, where the night's sites are staked with forked sticks for the torches or lanterns.

The river appears motionless, but a piece of driftwood lofted into the water betrays the persistent motion to the sea. Then comes a perceptible change in the atmosphere. With an eerie lack of warning and in absolute silence, the heaps of bankside driftwood and debris begin to disintegrate and move rapidly upstream with the advancing tide. The elvering nets are carefully lowered into the water, submerged and lifted. The night's harvesting has begun.

Severn elvers can be taken at any time of day or night when the tide is right, but the main hauls are made in darkness for elvers are largely photophobic, and daylight sends them to the bottom to hide. So it is principally night and gloaming tides which people the river bank with fishermen, their lights gleaming in the water, and, if the night is cold, driftwood fires burning well back on the banks. The elvers travel in huge shoals, moving further upstream with each successive tide, carried forward by the momentum of the water as well as their own astonishingly energetic, corkscrew locomotion. The elverer lowers his net into the dark, hurrying river, lifts it with the water cascading through the cheese cloth, and empties the elvers into a pail or bath. Sometimes the main shoals of elvers are too far out in the stream for the net to reach, and the vigil has to be extended to the ebb. Then the elvers invariably move in closer to the bank to escape the fast main current threatening to carry them back seawards.

Hauls can be enormous. Three scoops of the net can fill a bucket, and up to a quarter of a ton has been taken by a champion fisherman in an hour of exhausting, repetitive exploitation of an exceptionally rich elvering tide.

Occasionally, elvers enter the river at an unusually early date and are taken in substantial quantities in early February. The reasons for bumper elver harvests are conjectural, though Severnsiders believe the elvers are always most abundant in an early, warm spring. But the boffins explain the periodicity of Severnside elver booms in terms of distant oceanic conditions, which affect the elvers as they are carried westwards on the ocean currents in the larval stage.

The numbers of elvers taken each spring from the Severn are astronomical. They are also taken in substantial quantities from the Parrett near Bridgwater, as well as the Wye, the Usk and a few other rivers, but the hauls bear no comparison with those of the Severn.

There are approximately 1,000 elvers to the pound (slightly fewer when they enter the river, well nourished and plump after their oceanic migration), which means that each ton taken removes about two million elvers from the river. First elvers are fleshy, more or less transparent, 2–3in long and still very slightly flattened with characteristic, disproportionately large, leaf-shaped heads. At this stage elvers are at their best for the cooking bonanzas in riverside villages which mark their progress upstream.

There are many ways of preparing Severn elvers, but the commonest method is to wash off the river slime, scour them in salt water and then beat in a couple of eggs prior to frying them in butter as a sort of elver omelette. Alternatively, they are simply cooked in bacon fat. Writing in 1779, Samuel Rudder, the Gloucestershire historian, describes how 'the country people skim them up in great abundance, scour and boil them and bring them to market as white as snow where they usually sell at about two pence a pound'. In disappointing contrast to their succulent predecessors, late-season elvers become darkly pigmented, and are tough and unappetising.

The harvest is celebrated in some riverside villages with elver-eating contests, one of which purports to have the status of an annual world championship. However, in most years there is a notable absence of contestants from outside Gloucestershire. Whether your view of the world stops at the county borders or not, and whatever you wish to call it, the event is staged on the village green of Frampton-on-Severn each Easter Monday. The current elver-guzzling virtuoso is a burly Gloucestershire farmer who ate 900 elvers in 43 seconds. The leading lady has gulped down 600 elvers in just

At dusk, as the elvers move upstream on the evening tide, the fisherman prepares to submerge his elvering net

under a minute. These Easter Monday bunfights provide a good market for the local elverers who hawk their produce at good prices.

Apart from riverside housewives, West Country elver catchers have a lucrative market in gourmets who come from Bristol and elsewhere to buy them by the writhing pound, as well as in deep freeze merchants and the occasional discriminating fishmonger. Interest is not, however, confined to Britain alone. As long ago as 1908, a German firm was granted permission to establish an 'elver station' at the Anchor Inn, in the riverside village of Epney. The object was the export of live elvers to restock German rivers, particularly those flowing into the North and Baltic seas. These rivers are largely by-passed by the migrating elver billions. Large numbers of elvers were despatched annually to Germany in the early years, and the same elver station, closed during World War I, was again opened in the early twenties and remained operational until 1939, a period during which exports of four and a half million elvers a year were recorded.

During the fifties and early sixties, the Epney station was owned by a Billingsgate firm specialising in jellied eels. Each spring, two shrewd Cockney businessmen arrived to start up the station behind the Inn, where the elver storage tanks with their pumped river water were situated. Elvering tides brought catchers from miles away to service the two buyers, who often

Severn elvers at their culinary best — flesh, translucent, 2–3in long — but an unhappy end to their three-year journey across the Atlantic

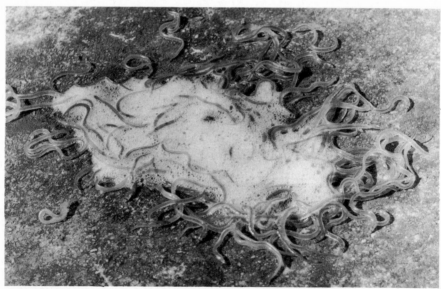

worked for a day and night without rest, paying out cash for the exportable produce of bumper tides which sometimes brought in a million elvers an hour. The elver station was sold but, with typical Cockney initiative, they then built another station for themselves further downstream. The elvers are exported to the continent in special triple-tier boxes, each with three compartments. Eight are packed with elvers, and the ninth contains a large sponge, soaked with river water to keep the elvers moist, and topped with a generous measure of ice to keep them cool.

Huge quantities of Severn elvers are now flown each spring from the elver station, not only to Europe, but also to densely populated Japan. The eel is an increasingly popular source of valuable protein, and it is estimated that 1lb of elvers, feeding and growing in ponds and watercourses, will yield 3 tons of mature fish in seven years. The four most nourishing kinds of fish are supposedly salmon, halibut, eel, and herring, but the eel is far and away the most prolific and cheapest of them.

The story of the three-year, three-thousand-mile journey which brings the elvers to the Severn is a truly epic one. Their deepwater odyssey begins in the seaweed-choked expanses of the Sargasso Sea. There, in the tomb and womb of all European eels, the adults that have made their way from the rivers and ponds of Europe, spawn and die 500 fathoms down. Immediately after hatching, the billions of tiny larvae begin their perilous current-borne journey back to Europe. They travel at 300 fathoms, washed westwards until, by their third autumn, they are approaching the coasts of Europe, where the change from larvae into elvers begins.

The yawning mouth of the Severn offers a wide welcome to the approaching billions and receives them, probably in greater numbers than any other river in Europe, except perhaps the Lower Loire in France. The funnel-shaped Severn has also a long tidal range in which the conditions of progressively decreasing salinity meet ideally the changing metabolic needs of the metamorphosing larvae. The elvers entering the Severn are helped by the second highest and fastest tide of any estuary in the world (the only tide higher than the Severn being that of the Bay of Fundy). A small number probably remain and grow to maturity in the estuary, but most of them make their way upstream to populate watercourses and ditches. They will even travel overland on wet nights in the search for freshwater homes.

The blind, instinctive fury of the elver ascent and the astronomical numbers which are swept into it, produce co-operative physical feats which would be incredible if they had not been reliably observed. They have been seen clinging in glistening masses to the sides of the jetty walls at Sharpness dock, building a huge living ladder to scale the vertical, tide-soaked quay side, left wet by the tide. Here, the traditional way to harvest elvers is simply to let down a piece of stiffened, metal gauze and scrape the sides of the elver-covered walls.

Perhaps the most dramatic story comes from an old Severnside fisherman, who fished the estuary all his long life and was a living chronicle of its history, happenings and moods. He told of seeing elvers in the clearer upper reaches of the river, massed together in such vast cohesion that they were like a 'giant ship's hawser', a yard wide and extending for a quarter of a mile.

12 Dewponds

They appear with mysterious suddenness on the chalk downs – small saucers of water, unfed by springs and without any visible means of support. Known variously as 'dewponds', 'cloudponds' and, by the shepherds, 'mist ponds', some of them are a perennial feature of the land. One pond on the downland above Winterbourne Bishop was recorded at the end of the last century as being about a quarter of a mile from the shepherd Caleb's 'liberty' – that section of the downs where he was entitled to pasture his sheep. It is still there today.

This was of course long before the days of alkathene pipe, power pumps, artesian wells and deep boreholes. The downland farmer in need of a water-supply for his sheep had no alternative but to call on the craft of the maker of dewponds. Dewpond construction was regarded as a hereditary craft, and there were certain families which had long specialised in the provision of this form of mainly chalkland water-supply. The trade card for 1937 of one member of the 'dewpond families', Mr L. J. Smith of Well Head, Dunstable, Bedfordshire, carried the following rather breathless legend:

Dewponds
The art of genuine Dew Pond making has been successfully practiced by my forefathers for generations, the secret process having been handed down from father to son, for 250 years. These ponds condense and retain their own water and are largely used for watering horses, cattle and sheep etc. but in recent years I have successfully applied the process to Ornamental Water Construction whereby beautiful lakes can now be obtained on any high or low or dry position whereby the pleasures of wild duck shooting, boating, skating, swimming etc can now be enjoyed on the driest of sites and has no equal as a water supply in case of fire, without the aid of pumping it.

The ponds to which Mr. Smith refers in his rather mysterious mention of a 'secret process', are today found mainly on the chalk downs of Wiltshire, Dorset, Hampshire, Berkshire and Sussex, traditionally the home of the dewpond and the county which boasts the most. However, they are also a feature of certain areas of Yorkshire and Derbyshire, a chalkless county, as well as being found on carboniferous limestone hills such as the Mendips in Somerset.

Mr Smith's claim to a secret formula is an enticing one. But, while dewpond-making can legitimately be described as a rural craft limited to a few exponents, the 'secrecy' tag is little more than sales promotion, fuelled by the undeniable curiosity of these ponds.

Dewponds were, as their name suggests, traditionally accepted as ponds replenished by dew. Custom also had it that they never failed or dried up, even in the severest droughts. Among others, Rudyard Kipling acknowledged the constant character of the dewpond in a quatrain from 'The Five Nations':

> We have no waters to delight
> Our broad and brookless vales
> Only the dewpond on the height
> Unfed that never fails.

The dewponds about which Kipling and a number of others have written, vary considerably in size, but all have certain things in common. Firstly, with one important distinction, they share the same principles of construction. The depth of water is usually a minimum of 2ft 6in at the centre. This is achieved by making an excavation in the chalk about 6ft deep, with a slope of about 1 in 10 from the centre of the excavation to the pool rim. The diameter of most ponds is usually 45–60ft and most, especially those more recently constructed, are encircled by a collecting area 10–12ft wide.

This dewpond near Salisbury has been servicing cattle and sheep for over fifty years. These mystifying ponds materialise unexpectedly on the waterless chalkland heights

Thus all dewponds shaped as they are rather like flattish cones, satisfy the first hydrographic principle of having a collecting and storing area which is considerably larger than the area of evaporation.

Because water flows through chalk as it does through the gills of a fish, the first priority is to ensure that the base of the pond is completely watertight. Concrete and asphalt recommend themselves as obvious base materials, and there are dewponds of fairly recent construction which have made use of them. Nevertheless, many dewpond craftsmen never used anything but clay, which they could make as watertight as the best concrete or tar. To achieve this hermetic seal, the wet clay was put on layer by layer and, as each was applied, it was beaten and consolidated with a 'puddling iron' until the various thin layers coalesced into a dense, impervious mass. As the layers were applied and puddled, they were laced with lime or soot to prevent the intrusion of earthworms. The finished clay floor, always at least 6in thick, was finally polished with the shiny steel face of the puddling iron until it formed a gleaming, unbroken conglomerate. Some dewpond-makers then applied the worm-repelling lime as a separate layer, $1\frac{1}{2}$–2in thick, on top of the polished clay.

There was no disagreement among dewpond-makers over this stage of construction, but there was certainly controversy over the next. Some dewpond makers asserted the absolute necessity of placing a 6in layer of straw on top of the lime or limed clay. The dewpond-makers of Wiltshire argued that this layer of wheat straw was absolutely indispensable for 'heat insulation', while those of Sussex and Dorset said straw was unnecessary and never used it. The insulation theory – insulation against what, one asks – was as flimsy as the quickly rotting material on which it was founded. A more likely justification for the use of the straw is that it prevented the puddled clay drying out too rapidly and, in winter, provided protection against fracturing frost. It may also have been designed to protect the sealed clay base against sharp stones from the flinty, chalk rubble which formed the next layer of material. This rubble, from the initial excavation, was invariably put back to form a final layer at least a foot thick. It was well beaten down and consolidated to ensure that the hooves of drinking animals did not penetrate the watertight clay seal. The dewpond was now complete and ready to receive water.

This is the point where the dewpond controversy really takes off. Where on these waterless, permeable chalk heights does dewpond water originate? According to one of the many parsons who inevitably become involved in this type of argument, the dewpond was first filled by piling snow round the collecting margin during the winter. The snow melted into the pond which then kept itself replenished. From what source comes the derisive cry? This is a problem on which one would certainly expect the doyen of nature commentators, Gilbert White, to hold an opinion, especially since he was also a man of the cloth. In his *Natural History of Selborne*, he says of those 'little ponds on the summit of chalk hills':

> Now we have many such little round ponds in this district and one in particular on our sheep down, three hundred feet above my house: which though never above three feet in the middle and not more than thirty feet in diameter and containing perhaps not more than two or three hundred hogsheads of water, yet never is known to fail, though it affords drink for three hundred or four hundred sheep, and for at least twenty head of large cattle beside. This pond, it is true, is over-hung with two moderate beeches, that, doubtless, at times afford it much supply: but then we have others as small, that, without the aid of trees, and in spite of evaporation from sun and wind, and perpetual consumption by cattle, yet constantly maintain a moderate share of water, without overflowing in the wettest seasons, as they would do if supplied by springs . . . Dr. Hales, in his *Vegetable Statics*, advances, from experiment, that 'the moister the earth is the more dew falls on it in a night: and more than a double quantity of dew falls on a surface of water than there does on an equal surface of moist earth.' Hence we see that water, by its coolness, is enabled to assimilate to itself a large quantity of moisture nightly by condensation; and that the air, when loaded with fogs and vapours, and even with copious dews, can alone advance a considerable and never-failing resource.

Dew has three sources. It 'falls' when moisture-laden air above the ground reaches dewpoint, and condenses its moisture on the night-cooled earth. It 'rises' when moisture-laden air rising from the interstices of the soil similarly reaches dewpoint and condenses. Finally, some part of the moisture which washes the early-rising countryman's boots as he walks through grass after a rainless night is derived from the transpiration of plants – the exhalation of water vapour from the pores of leaves and stems. How then do these facts fit Gilbert White's notion?

In the first place, it is obvious that the dewpond cannot be replenished by 'rising dew', because the clay or concrete bottom in all successful ponds has to be watertight. Secondly, most dewponds have little or no vegetation round their margins, and it is extremely unlikely that the transpiration of any plants around the collecting margins could be a major source of water replenishment. Gilbert White in his explanation mentions the contribution of drops of water from dripping trees and shrubs, especially after heavy fogs and mists, but as he also adds most dewponds, on the chalk downs at least, are bare and barren of surrounding trees.

So one is left with 'falling dew' as the only other possible source of this kind. This theory stands or falls by the thermometer. If the surface of the dewpond is in fact colder than the surrounding ground, then, the moisture-laden atmosphere will condense into water when it comes into contact with the surface of the pond, and thus contribute to its replenishment.

Unfortunately – for dew replenishment is an attractive notion – this idea does not hold water either. Water has a thermal capacity five times that of dry soil, which means that the temperature of the dewpond is almost always higher than that of the surrounding soil, except perhaps for a brief period at night when the temperature evens out. The earth stores more solar heat than the dewpond, but loses it much faster during the night, and quickly drops to a temperature lower than that of the surface of water. So, during the night when dew is produced, virtually all 'falling dew' will be deposited on the earth surrounding the dewpond, not in the pond itself.

Lastly there is 'mist'. Mist as a source of dewpond water has had support from a number of amateur meteorologists. Certainly, to anyone who has experienced the soaking, obliterating mists which billow from the sea onto the South Downs in autumn and winter, this is a more creditable hypothesis. This theory of replenishment on the South Downs was given additional credence by analyses which showed that dewponds on these downs contained a relatively high percentage of salt. However, the presence of salt in the water of dewponds in coastal areas need have nothing to do with mist. It signifies merely the picking up of particles of salt by the prevailing winds, which may be deposited, and a progressively increasing concentration of salt may build up in the ponds as a result of evaporation. There is no hard evidence to support the notion of mist as a major source of replenishment.

There remains only rain as the other possible source of supply for the dewpond. This proposition was first made by one of those contentious parsons. Its validity depends on whether enough rain falls in the traditional dewpond areas to keep them replenished. Surprisingly perhaps, in view of its importance as our chief corn-growing region with its concomitant need for good harvesting weather, much of our chalk downland lies in the 40in rainfall belt. This means that there is an annual fall of water equivalent to 3500–4000 tons of water on every acre of land, and it is on this relatively high annual rainfall that the dewpond has to depend for replenishment.

So all successful dewponds are constructed to collect and store as much of the available rain as possible. The collecting surface of the traditional dewpond is always made roughly twice that of the evaporation area. Secondly, the gradient of the dewpond, from the rim to the centre, ensures that the ratio of water volume to surface area is always high, so that evaporation by the sun is reduced. Thirdly, the white, puddled flint of the clay base ensures that there is minimum absorption of heat. Light-coloured surfaces are the most efficient reflectors of radiant heat, so that heat absorption and evaporation are correspondingly reduced.

The 'secret' formula claimed by certain 'dewpond families' is, then, the craftsman's recognition and observance of elementary laws which govern the deposition and evaporation of rainwater. Dewponds are no more than simple catchment ponds for rain. The scientist's truth is, alas, always more prosaic than the countryman's fiction.

Nevertheless, the word 'dewpond' survives and will undoubtedly continue to describe these entrancing little saucers of rain. There is something very compelling about the notion of harnessing dew. As the sign of dawn, with which the new day is anointed, dew has always been a favourite word with the early-rising countryman. Traditionally his pre-breakfast snack was always the 'dew bit'; the first morning-allowance of beer or cider at harvest-time, the 'dew cup'; the rainbow seen in dewdrops, the 'dew bow'; the dew-pearled creation of the night-spinning spider, the 'dew web'.

Thus, despite the harsh facts – the yield of water from all dew deposited on the chalk downs amounts, on average, to less than 1in per year – the gentle tradition prevails. Dewponds they are, and dewponds they will remain.

Bibliography

Chapter 1
Florance, N. Rushwork (1962)

Chapter 2
Austin, J. G. The Straw Plaiting and Straw Hat and Bonnet Trade (1871)
Freeman, C. Luton and the Straw Hat Industry (1953)
Percival, J. Wheat in Great Britain (1933)
Rural Industries Bureau The Thatcher's Craft (1961)
Stowe, E. Crafts of the Countryside (1948)

Chapter 3
Warden, J. The Linen Trade (1963)

Chapter 4
Landsborough, D. L. A Popular History of British Seaweeds
Hampson, M. A. The Laverbread Industry in South Wales (1958)
Newton, L. Seaweed Utilisation (1951)

Chapter 5
Marshall, W. The Rural Economy of the Southern Counties (1798)
Ministry of Agriculture and Fisheries Hop Growing and Drying (1967)

Chapter 6
Cooke, C. W. Radcliffe A book about Cider and Perry (1898)
Durham, H. E. Journal of Royal Horticultural Society (1924)
Long Ashton Research Station Memorial Volume to Professor B. T. P. Barker Perry Pears (1963)
Marshall, W. The Rural Economy of Gloucestershire etc and the Management of Orchards and Fruit Liquor in Herefordshire (1789)

Chapter 7
Victoria History of Counties of England History of Somerset (1911)
Young, A. Farmer's Tour Through the East of England (1770)

Chapter 8
British Pharmacopoeia 1932
Grieve, M. A Modern Herbal (1931)
Trease, G. E. Textbook of Pharmacognosy (1945)

Chapter 9
Brighton, C. W. Quarterly Journal of Forestry (1951)
Forestry Commission Cultivation of Cricket Bat Willow (1968)
Long Ashton Research Station, University of Bristol Annual Reports (1930–38)

Chapter 10
Long Ashton Research Station Annual Reports, 1954–62
Scientific Horticulture 1956

Chapter 11
Taylor J. Neufville Illustrated Guide to Severn Fishery Collection (1953)
Victoria History of Counties of Britain History of Gloucestershire (1911)
Waters, B. Severn Tide

Chapter 12
Hubbard A. J. & G. Neolithic Dewponds and Cattle Ways
Martin, E. A. Dewponds, History, Observation and Experiment (1915)
Pugsley, A. J. Dewponds (1938)
Slade, A. P. Dewponds (1877)
White, Gilbert Natural History of Selbourne

Index